EMMA

A PLAY BY

GORDON GLENNON

FROM THE NOVEL BY

JANE AUSTEN

LONDON
MACMILLAN & CO. LTD
1945

Jane lies in Winchester—blessed be her shade!
Praise the Lord for making her, and her for all she made.

RUDYARD KIPLING

PRINTED IN GREAT BRITAIN
BY R. & R. CLARK, LIMITED, EDINBURGH

First produced at Rugby Repertory Theatre on August 24th, 1943, subsequently presented by Robert Donat on 7th February 1945 at The St. James's Theatre, London, with the following cast:

Emma	Anna Neagle
Mr. Knightley	Frank Allenby
Mr. Woodhouse	Graveley Edwards
Mr. Elton	George Thirlwell
Mrs. Elton	Ambrosine Phillpotts
Mr. Weston	Cecil Ramage
Mrs. Weston	Wynn Clark
Miss Bates	Gillian Lind
Jane Fairfax	Margaret Vines
Frank Churchill	Grey Blake
Harriet Smith	Terry Randal
Serle	H. R. Hignett

CHARACTERS

EMMA WOODHOUSE

MR. WOODHOUSE, *her father*

MR. KNIGHTLEY, *whose brother is married to Emma's sister*

MRS. WESTON, *Emma's late governess, now her neighbour and dearest friend*

MR. WESTON, *Mrs. Weston's husband*

FRANK CHURCHILL, *Mr. Weston's son by an earlier marriage: adopted by his aunt, whose name he has assumed*

JANE FAIRFAX

MISS BATES, *Jane's aunt*

MR. ELTON, *the new Vicar at Highbury*

MRS. ELTON

HARRIET SMITH, *Emma's young companion*

SERLE, *butler*

ACT I

An Afternoon early in the year 1815

The drawing-room at Hartfield, the Woodhouses' residence in Highbury, a village near London. A charming house in the Regency style; tastefully yet comfortably furnished, it is both dignified and cheerful.

The large double doors lead out to a spacious hall. The only other doors in the room are those of the french windows which lead to the garden.

Down-stage, near the fireplace, seated at the backgammon table is MRS. WESTON, *a sensible woman of five-and-thirty years. Opposite her is* MR. WOODHOUSE, *a frail old gentleman who enjoys his own ill-health and the ill-health of all his friends. He studies the game and moves his counter.*

MR. WOODHOUSE. Come, Mrs. Weston, let us see what you can do against that, madam.

MRS. WESTON (*shakes the dice*). I declare my luck seems quite to have deserted me. (*She throws.*) Oh, there, what did I say? Now you cannot help but beat me. (*She moves her counter.*)

MR. WOODHOUSE. You give in too easily, madam, we have but started the game.

MRS. WESTON. Your throw, sir.

MR. WOODHOUSE. Let us not hurry too much. There is no pleasure in a game that is hurried. (*Relaxes in his chair.*) Is that not so, Miss Taylor?

MRS. WESTON. Yes, indeed, sir — but you must

not forget that I am Mrs. Weston now.

MR. WOODHOUSE. Alas, I cannot help but remember it. How happy we all were when you were here, Miss Taylor! How happy we all were but a short time ago!

MRS. WESTON. Come, sir, surely you do not grudge me a home of my own and an affectionate, devoted husband.

MR. WOODHOUSE. Oh, I do not grudge anyone their happiness, if that is what they are after, but it seems to me that we were very well content as we were.

MRS. WESTON. You are all kindness to miss me so much, sir, and believe me, I miss both you and Emma in spite of my happiness with Mr. Weston.

MR. WOODHOUSE. Well, what are we waiting for? Have you lost interest in the game, madam?

MRS. WESTON (*smiles to herself*). No, indeed, sir. Is it my play?

MR. WOODHOUSE. Certainly, madam. Pray do not be so slow.

Enter SERLE.

SERLE. Mr. Knightley to see you, sir.

Enter MR. KNIGHTLEY. *He is about thirty-five years old, handsome and intelligent. He gives the impression of a strong character and deep sincerity.*

MR. WOODHOUSE. Mr. Knightley, is it?

MR. KNIGHTLEY. Good afternoon, sir. Mrs. Weston. (*Bows.*)

MRS. WESTON. Sir.

MR. KNIGHTLEY. How are you both to-day?

MR. WOODHOUSE. We are in the middle of a game.

MR. KNIGHTLEY. I came to have my revenge

after last night's defeat, but I see I have been forestalled.

MR. WOODHOUSE. You are very good to come and play a game with me when Emma is out visiting Miss Smith. You too, Miss Taylor, both are good. (*Nods sleepily.*)

MRS. WESTON. I have to meet Mr. Weston at the Crown before the hour. Shall we finish the game, sir? (*Holds out shaker.*)

MR. WOODHOUSE. Pray let us not hurry, madam. That is what I am always saying to Emma. There is no pleasure in a game that is hurried: particularly backgammon. (*Nods.*)

MR. KNIGHTLEY. And if I know Emma, sir, there is no pleasure for her in anything that is not hurried. Her mind is like quicksilver as it darts from one thing to another.

MR. WOODHOUSE (*sleepily*). She has ever been the same since she stood no higher than this table. (*His head drops.*)

MR. KNIGHTLEY. So Emma has gone to visit Miss Smith, has she?

MRS. WESTON (*nods*). Look. (*Indicates* MR. WOODHOUSE.)

MR. KNIGHTLEY. Poor Mr. Woodhouse. How quickly he gets exhausted nowadays.

MRS. WESTON. He sleeps restless when the light is in his eyes.

Crosses to MR. WOODHOUSE, *places his handkerchief gently over his face.*

MR. KNIGHTLEY. Shall I finish his game for him?

MRS. WESTON. That would be a pleasure. I should just have time.

MR. KNIGHTLEY *moves table, and fetches a*

chair. The ensuing scene is all the time punctuated with the movements of the game.

MR. KNIGHTLEY. Tell me, madam, what is your opinion of this intimacy between Emma and Harriet Smith? I do not altogether approve of it.

MRS. WESTON. Oh, Mr. Knightley, why so?

MR. KNIGHTLEY. Because in my opinion it will not do either of them any good. Emma is in need of someone stronger than herself. Someone who will oppose her when necessary, and remind her constantly to leave off busying herself with other people's private emotions.

MRS. WESTON. Well, whatever you say, she has not gone far wrong yet, and I for one am not afraid for her.

MR. KNIGHTLEY. Oh, it is not Emma I am afraid for. It is the effect she will have on others. Do you know the latest thing? She informed me but the other day that she was responsible for bringing about the match between yourself and Mr. Weston.

MRS. WESTON (*good-naturedly*). I knew she had such an idea, but as it does me no harm, I let her think it.

MR. KNIGHTLEY. Nevertheless, she was wrong, as she always is, when she tries to match people off.

MRS. WESTON. We are all of us possessed of faults we should not like to be held to censure for. Emma's fault happens to be of match-making: let us be tolerant of it.

MR. KNIGHTLEY. Oh, do not mistake me, madam. Emma, perfect, would be dull: and dullness could not be Emma.

MRS. WESTON. How well she looked at my wedding! Every eye was on her.

MR. KNIGHTLEY. Ah, you would rather talk of her person than her mind. Very well, I shall not attempt to deny I have never seen a face or a figure more pleasing to me than Emma's.

MRS. WESTON. She is loveliness itself, Mr. Knightley, is she not?

MR. KNIGHTLEY (*carried away*). I love to look at her and I will add this praise: I do not think her personally vain considering how very handsome she is; she appears very little occupied with it. (*The game has come to an end.* MRS. WESTON *has won; she gets up and pulls the bell.*) See, you have beaten me; that is what I deserve for criticising Emma instead of studying the game.

MRS. WESTON. Mr. Woodhouse is still quite asleep. I must hurry off or I shall be late at the Crown.

MR. KNIGHTLEY (*rises, moves* U.C.). I will walk some part of the way with you.

MRS. WESTON. Thank you, sir. (SERLE *comes in.*) Oh, Serle, did Miss Woodhouse say what time she would be back?

SERLE. She did not specify in time, madam, but as she only went to Mrs. Goddard's, I do not think she will be long.

MRS. WESTON (*crosses* MR. KNIGHTLEY *to* L. *of* SERLE). Tell Miss Woodhouse, Serle, that I shall return after I have met Mr. Weston.

SERLE. Very good, madam.

MRS. WESTON. Serle, see that the fire does not die down on Mr. Woodhouse. You know how he feels the cold.

MR. KNIGHTLEY. The room stifles me already; come, let us get some fresh air.

They go out. SERLE *moves the backgammon table*

to U.L. *While he is doing this the french windows open.* SERLE *looks up and puts his finger to his lips to quieten* EMMA WOODHOUSE *who runs into the room.* EMMA *is vivacious and attractive, her personality is assured and lovable.*

EMMA. Serle! Serle! Oh, Serle!

SERLE. Hush, Miss Emma.

EMMA. Oh, Papa is asleep. Has Mrs. Weston gone away? (*Takes off her hat.*)

SERLE. She will return on her way home. Mr. Knightley has gone down the drive with her. (*He moves to doors.*)

EMMA. Thank you, Serle. Oh, before you go, please help me with this easel. (EMMA L. *of easel,* SERLE R.)

SERLE. Certainly, ma'am.

They bring the easel D.C. *The paint-box on the ledge falls off with a clatter and wakes* MR. WOODHOUSE.

MR. WOODHOUSE (*startled*). Who's there? What is it? Who is it? Oh, it's you, Emma!

EMMA *crosses to comfort her father.* SERLE *places the easel down-stage* R., *crosses back* C. *to pick up paint-box.*

EMMA. I am sorry to have wakened you, dear Papa. The paint-box fell off the easel.

MR. WOODHOUSE. You quite startled me, Emma. It is not good for an old man to be startled out of sleep. I feel quite of a tremble. (*Holds out hands.*)

EMMA. Shall Serle bring you some Madeira wine, Papa?

MR. WOODHOUSE. No, my love, perhaps a little thin gruel.

EMMA *crosses to* SERLE *and takes the paint-box.*

SERLE. I will see to it for you, sir.

MR. WOODHOUSE. Thank you, Serle.

EMMA *crosses up* L. *to cabinet for portrait. Serle follows and goes out.*

MR. WOODHOUSE. You are to be painting, I see. Where is little Miss Smith? Did you not go to fetch her?

EMMA. Harriet has stopped to speak with an acquaintance. She will be here directly. (*Goes to easel.*)

MR. WOODHOUSE. And where is Mr. Knightley, pray?

EMMA. He is only walking some way with Mrs. Weston.

MR. WOODHOUSE. That is what I must have, some exercise. An old man needs exercise.

EMMA. Yes, Papa.

MR. WOODHOUSE. If there is one thing I do not like, it is being rudely awakened.

He goes out. EMMA *smiles after him affectionately.*

EMMA. Dear Papa, it is ever the same after he has been to sleep. (*She crosses up* L. *to cabinet for apron from drawer, crosses* D.R. *again, putting it on.*)

HARRIET SMITH *runs in at the double door. She is fair and almost too pretty; she is inclined to simper and appears to have no mind of her own.*

EMMA. Oh, Harriet, there you are at last.

HARRIET. Pray forgive me, dear Miss Woodhouse (D.C.).

EMMA. Take off your things, Harriet, and let us begin at once.

HARRIET. Yes, Miss Woodhouse. Are you sure you wish to finish the portrait to-day?

EMMA. Decidedly, Harriet; is not that why I fetched you from Mrs. Goddard's?

HARRIET (*crosses above sofa, takes off things and puts on end* R.). Yes, indeed, Miss Woodhouse. I only hoped you might not be too tired.

EMMA. Dear Harriet, I am never tired. Take your place on the stool.

HARRIET *fetches stool from the back, places it* D.S.C. EMMA *crosses, poses* HARRIET'S *head and hand, crosses back to easel, then brings piano-stool to* D.R. HARRIET *fidgets.* EMMA *crosses and re-poses* HARRIET. EMMA *crosses back to easel and sits.* HARRIET *rises, crosses* C. *for handkerchief and back to sit.*

EMMA (*poised, brush in hand*). Pray, dear Harriet, how can I do justice to your beauty if you will fidget so? (*Dabs portrait with a flourish more graceful than professional.*)

HARRIET. Pray forgive me, dear Miss Woodhouse. I think I am not in the mood for sitting still to-day.

EMMA. Only a moment and I will have done your hair. It will not take long.

HARRIET. Yes, Miss Woodhouse. (*Pause.*)

EMMA. Harriet, who was the young gentleman you stopped to speak with at the gate?

HARRIET. Mr. Robert Martin of Abbey Mill Farm. I stayed there two months in the summer.

EMMA. Oh, a farmer. Not a man of education. I presume Mr. Martin does not read.

HARRIET. Oh yes; that is, I do not know. I

believe he has read *The Vicar of Wakefield* and I know he reads the Agricultural Reports.

EMMA. Dear Harriet, I must advise you. The misfortune of your birth should make you doubly careful in your choice of friends.

HARRIET. Mrs. Goddard says my father means to do well by me even if he did not do right by my mother.

EMMA. I am convinced you are the daughter of a gentleman whatever your unfortunate mother may have been.

HARRIET. Oh, Miss Woodhouse, I might be anyone's daughter.

EMMA. In fact I should not be at all surprised if your father were not a peer of the realm. They frequently make a mistake such as yourself.

HARRIET. Yes, Miss Woodhouse.

EMMA. Indeed it is sometimes the case even with royalty.

HARRIET. Is it not an exciting mystery? Only think——

EMMA. And now, we must find you a suitable husband, a gentleman of rank and understanding. (*Rises.*) There, you may relax. Tell me, what do you think of Mr. Elton? (*Puts down paint-box, crosses* C., *taking off apron.*)

HARRIET. He seems a very pretty young gentleman, a very pretty gentleman indeed.

EMMA. He is more than a little attached to you, my dear, who knows what might not happen. (*Crosses to cabinet, puts apron away.*)

HARRIET (*crosses* U.C. *to* R. *of* EMMA *with stool*). You mean *he* wishes to marry me? The new Vicar wishes to marry me as well.

EMMA. Oh, come, Harriet, I merely hinted that he was attached to you. (*After thought.*) What do you mean by " as well "?

Both move D.C.

HARRIET. I do not know how to tell you, Miss Woodhouse. It was not by accident we met Mr. Martin. He was waiting for me with a letter — (*fumbles in her pocket*) — this letter.

EMMA. And what is in the letter, pray?

HARRIET (*hesitating*). An offer of marriage.

EMMA. Such presumption.

HARRIET. He writes as if he loves me very much. I need your advice, dear Miss Woodhouse; what shall I do?

EMMA. Upon my word, the young man is determined to better himself if he can.

HARRIET. Will you read the letter, dear Miss Woodhouse, and tell me what I ought to answer?

EMMA. Oh no, the answer had much better be your own, only, whatever you do, do not write with appearance of sorrow for his disappointment.

HARRIET (*looking down*). You think I ought to refuse him, then?

EMMA. My dear Harriet, what do you mean? Are you in any doubt? But I beg your pardon, perhaps I have been under a mistake. (HARRIET *is silent. In tones of shocked surprise*) You mean to return a favourable answer?

HARRIET (*hands* EMMA *the letter*). Pray, dear Miss Woodhouse, tell me what I ought to do. Read his letter and tell me what I ought to do.

EMMA. This is a point you must settle with your own feeling. However, I will read the letter if you wish.

EMMA *takes letter, crosses to sofa and sits, reads letter.* HARRIET *watches her anxiously.*

HARRIET (*crosses to sit* L. *of* EMMA *on sofa*). Well, is it a good sort of letter, or is it too short?

EMMA (*with some thought*). Yes, indeed, a very good letter; (*rises, crosses* C.) so good a letter, Harriet, that I think one of his sisters must have helped him. (*Reconsiders.*) Yet it is hardly a woman's style. Yes, a better written letter than I should have expected.

HARRIET. I had no notion he liked me so much — if only I knew what my feelings were.

EMMA. Do not imagine that I want to influence you, Harriet, but I lay it down as a general rule, that if a woman *doubts* whether she should accept a man or not, she certainly ought to refuse him. (*Returns letter.*)

HARRIET (*petulantly, dithering as if she were choosing a hat*). It is so very serious a thing to decide. Perhaps it would be safer to say no. (*Rises, crosses* C.) Do you think that I had better say no?

EMMA (*smiling graciously*). Not for the world would I advise you either way.

HARRIET (*crosses to fireplace*). As you will not give me your opinion, Miss Woodhouse, I have almost made up my mind to refuse Mr. Martin. Do you think I am right?

EMMA (*delighted*). Perfectly, perfectly right, my dearest Harriet. Now you have so completely decided, I have no hesitation in approving. It would have grieved me to lose your acquaintance, which must have been the consequence if you had married Mr. Martin.

HARRIET. Lose your acquaintance! Oh, Miss

Woodhouse, it would have killed me never to come to Hartfield any more.

EMMA. Dear, affectionate creature; we shall not be parted. A woman is not to marry a man merely because she is asked, or because he can write a tolerable letter.

HARRIET. Oh no, and it is such a short letter too. Nobody cares for a letter.

SERLE *enters.*

EMMA. What is it, Serle?

SERLE. Mr. Elton, madam.

EMMA (*to* HARRIET, *excitedly*). Mr. Elton! What did I not tell you? Show him in, Serle. Is Mr. Knightley returned yet?

SERLE. He is in the library with Mr. Woodhouse, ma'am.

He bows and goes out.

EMMA. Mr. Elton must have known you would be here. (*She arranges a bow in* HARRIET'S *hair.*) Harriet, I have a plan. You must stay here for a visit. I shall send a note to Mrs. Goddard's directly, and you must go and fetch your clothes.

HARRIET. Oh, dear Miss Woodhouse. That I, Harriet Smith, the daughter of somebody, or nobody, should be staying with the foremost family in Highbury.

EMMA. With your looks and charm, dear Harriet, you will go further than any girl in Mrs. Goddard's school in spite of — well, everything.

SERLE *comes in followed by* MR. ELTON. *He is about twenty-eight years old, rather delicate-looking and somewhat colourless in appearance. His manner is a cross between servility and smooth-tongued cunning.*

MR. ELTON. My dear Miss Woodhouse, and your charming little friend. How are you both to-day?

HARRIET *bobs.*

EMMA. In excellent spirits, Mr. Elton. (*Crosses to easel.*) Come, we have something to show you.

MR. ELTON. The portrait is finished? (*Crossing to easel, above sofa.*)

EMMA. Not above five minutes ago.

MR. ELTON *moves round to the picture enthusiastically.*

EMMA. Well, is it a fair likeness, Mr. Elton?

EMMA *above sofa* — HARRIET D.C.

MR. ELTON (*looking from the portrait to* HARRIET *and back again to the portrait*). Superb, an excellent likeness, the delicate tints have a beauty of their own. Exactly the shade of her pale-gold hair, the gentle blue of her eyes, the soft bloom of her complexion. You have caught so perfectly the shape of the eye and the gentle curve of her beautiful mouth. A little masterpiece, Miss Woodhouse. I never saw such a likeness in my life.

EMMA. You are too kind, Mr. Elton. See how you have made Harriet blush, she has so little opinion of her own beauty.

MR. ELTON (*gazing at* HARRIET). Modesty, a charming trait. Dear Miss Woodhouse, we must have it framed at once.

EMMA. Yes, indeed.

MR. ELTON. If I may be entrusted with the commission, I shall take it myself to London in the morning.

HARRIET. You are indeed too kind, sir.

MR. ELTON. So rare a jewel must have the perfect setting. I myself shall choose the frame.

EMMA. You are too gallant, sir.

MR. ELTON. To be employed on such an errand will give me infinite pleasure. (*With a sigh he looks at the portrait.*) What a precious deposit.

HARRIET *giggles.*

EMMA (*moves to* HARRIET, C.). Dear Harriet is overcome by your goodness, Mr. Elton.

MR. ELTON. What man could not be honoured to serve two such lovely ladies. Perfection!

EMMA. Come, sir, I shall blush myself directly.

MR. ELTON. A lady's blushes do but portray the tenderness of her disposition, and now with your permission I shall pay my respects to dear Mr. Woodhouse. Some local business. What the parish of Highbury should do without its bountiful Mr. Woodhouse, I cannot imagine.

EMMA. Papa is in the library. Come, sir, I will take you to him. Do not go, Harriet, I shall return at once. (*They go to the door, which* MR. ELTON *opens and stands aside for* EMMA *to pass through.* HARRIET *smiles after* MR. ELTON, *then, left alone, she gazes at Mr. Martin's letter longingly, slips it into her bosom and begins to cry.* EMMA *comes in and puts her arms round* HARRIET *comfortingly,* R. of HARRIET, *who is kneeling by fire.*) Dearest Harriet, this will never do. Come, dry those tears and smile again.

HARRIET (*between sobs*). Poor Mr. Martin, so truly kind and gentle he was at Abbey Mill last summer.

EMMA. Do not forget Mr. Martin is young, he will soon forget; before we know it, we shall be hearing of his consoling himself with someone nearer his own station.

HARRIET. Oh, Miss Woodhouse, do you think we

shall? I am not at all sure that I should like to hear that.

EMMA (*rises*). Harriet, what do you mean?

HARRIET. I should not like him to choose hastily, only for the sake of consolation.

HARRIET *rises*.

EMMA. There again, as always, you consider others before yourself; you are too *kind*-hearted by far. If you had but heard Mr. Elton singing your praises just now, your tears would soon be dry.

HARRIET (*almost smiling*). Mr. Elton is indeed a very fine sort of gentleman, is he not, Miss Woodhouse?

EMMA. If you could only have but heard him. (*Imitates* ELTON.) Such a delicate beauty, like a flower. So excellent a friend for you, dear Miss Woodhouse.

HARRIET. Indeed I am glad he should think so.

EMMA. I wager he takes your picture directly to his mother and sisters to-morrow before the night is out, and tells them how much more beautiful is the original.

HARRIET'S *face clears and she smiles*.

HARRIET. I hope they will not be too disappointed when we should meet.

EMMA. The Vicarage is quite charming, and if it were not for the garden I should say it was perfection. Though what house that has Harriet Smith for a mistress needs a garden? Or should I say Harriet Elton?

HARRIET (*crosses* EMMA *to* D.C. *Smiles at the thought*). The Vicarage is indeed a pleasant house, with such a commanding view of the Churchyard.

EMMA. Let us dwell on pleasanter things. While

I write a letter to Mrs. Goddard, off you go and collect your clothes.

HARRIET. Dearest Miss Woodhouse, you are all kindness.

EMMA. The carriage will bring you back. My tender-hearted little friend, go now and come back quickly.

HARRIET. I shall never be able to repay your goodness to me.

She goes out. EMMA *crosses to the picture, looks at it affectionately.*

EMMA (*speaking to the picture*). One day, dear Harriet, you will be truly grateful for my counsel. I think it will not be long before you are Mistress at the Vicarage. I am sure Mr. Elton is desperately in love. What a strange thing love must be. (*Moves to the writing-desk, looks in the mirror and talks to her own reflection.*) There is little doubt, Emma Woodhouse, you have a happy talent for match-making. (*She sits down and proceeds to write for a few moments, then stops.*) How charming Harriet is when she smiles, and how her smiles grew stronger as I told her of Mr. Elton's praises. Soon she will have forgotten how fond she is of the loutish Mr. Martin. (*She continues to write. The door opens and* MR. WOODHOUSE *comes in, wrapped up in a heavy overcoat and scarf. He is accompanied by* MR. ELTON *on one side, and* MR. KNIGHTLEY *on the other.* MR. WOODHOUSE *to* U.C. MR. KNIGHTLEY R., MR. ELTON L. *of him. Rising*) Papa, are you going out?

MR. WOODHOUSE. Yes, my love, while the sun is shining, if Mr. Knightley will excuse me I shall take a turn round. You will not think me rude, sir? We invalids are privileged people.

MR. KNIGHTLEY. My dear sir, do not make a stranger of me.

MR. WOODHOUSE. Emma will be happy to entertain you. Mr. Elton is most kind in saying he will accompany me some part of the way.

MR. ELTON. A call I have to make on Mr. Weston — a business call, parish business — it will not take me long. With your permission I shall return and collect the treasured possession.

MR. WOODHOUSE. So you are calling on Mr. Weston next. A good citizen. I have nothing against him, except for his marrying poor Miss Taylor.

MR. ELTON. Miss Taylor?

EMMA. Papa means Mrs. Weston.

MR. ELTON. Oh, Mrs. Weston is a charming lady.

MR. WOODHOUSE. I was only about to recover from losing my Isabella to your brother, Mr. Knightley, and then Mr. Weston comes and takes away Miss Taylor.

EMMA (*to* MR. ELTON, *who looks puzzled*). Isabella is my sister, Mr. Elton. She is married to Mr. John Knightley.

MR. ELTON. Ah, now I understand. How trying it is to be a stranger in a community until one finds one's way about.

MR. WOODHOUSE. Marriage is a curse, sir, a curse it is. (*Crosses to* EMMA.) Well, as long as someone does not try to steal my Emma, I shall not mind so much.

EMMA. You need not fear, Papa, I shall never marry.

MR. KNIGHTLEY. I think otherwise, Emma. I have no doubt that you will marry.

MR. ELTON. I agree, sir. What are the charming lines of the poet: " Full many a flower is born to blush unseen, And waste its sweetness on the desert air ".

MR. KNIGHTLEY. Well said, sir.

MR. ELTON. That must not happen in your case, dear Miss Woodhouse.

MR. WOODHOUSE. Pray, do not put such ideas of discontent into Emma's head, gentlemen, I beg you.

EMMA (*deliberately changing the subject*). Come, this has gone far enough. Papa, here is Harriet's portrait. I have finished it.

MR. ELTON. So truly an artist as Miss Woodhouse is, scarcely a brush-mark showing.

She leads MR. WOODHOUSE *to easel.* MR. KNIGHTLEY *has already been examining it without comment.* MR. WOODHOUSE *and* MR. ELTON *gaze at the picture.*

MR. WOODHOUSE. It is a very pretty water-colour. So prettily done. (*Crosses to* EMMA.) The only thing I do not like is that she seems to be sitting out of doors. It makes one think she must catch cold.

EMMA (L. *of* MR. WOODHOUSE). But, dear Papa, it is supposed to be summer. A warm day in summer. Look at the tree.

MR. WOODHOUSE. But it is never safe to sit out of doors, my dear, even on the warmest day, not even at a strawberry-gathering party.

MR. ELTON (*crosses* D.R.). I regard it as a most happy thought placing Miss Smith out of doors; and see, Mr. Woodhouse, the tree is touched with such inimitable spirit. Oh, it is most admirable. I cannot keep my eyes from it.

MR. KNIGHTLEY. I do not think her height is in

proportion. Miss Smith is not so elegant as Emma has aspired to make her.

MR. ELTON. Oh no; it gives one exactly the idea of such a height as Miss Smith's. Exactly so, indeed.

EMMA. You waste your time in defending me, Mr. Elton. Mr. Knightley loves to find fault with me.

MR. KNIGHTLEY. Emma knows I never flatter her.

EMMA. We always say exactly what we like to one another.

MR. WOODHOUSE. They squabble like a brother and sister, Mr. Elton. Pay them no attention.

MR. KNIGHTLEY. I should not want Emma for a sister, sir.

EMMA (*with spirit*). Nor should I want you for a brother, sir.

MR. WOODHOUSE. Come, Mr. Elton, let us go before the sun will have gone down.

MR. ELTON. At your service, sir.

MR. WOODHOUSE (*at door*). Look after my Emma, Mr. Knightley. Do not let her catch cold.

MR. KNIGHTLEY. Emma is always safe with me, sir.

MR. ELTON. I will return directly, dear Miss Woodhouse. (*He looks at the picture, then at* EMMA, *sighs, and follows* MR. WOODHOUSE *out.*)

EMMA (*returning to the writing-desk*). Permit me to finish this note; it should have gone long ago.

MR. KNIGHTLEY. By all means. (EMMA *continues to write. He seats himself where he can look at the picture; turning easel to face* R. *end of sofa, sits on arm of sofa.*) Yes, I cannot rate her beauty as you do, but she is a pretty creature and I am inclined to think well of her disposition.

EMMA. You are more than generous, sir.

MR. KNIGHTLEY. Her character depends on those she is with, but in good hands she will turn out a sensible woman.

EMMA. I am glad you think so, and the good hands, I hope, will not be wanting.

MR. KNIGHTLEY. Come, you are anxious for a compliment, so I will give you one. I *do* think you have improved her. You have almost cured her of that abominable schoolgirl giggle, and her style and deportment, so newly acquired, do you ample credit.

EMMA. You are generosity personified, sir.

MR. KNIGHTLEY. Emma, I have reason to think that Harriet Smith will soon have an offer of marriage.

EMMA (*excited*). Has someone dropped a hint while you gentlemen were in the library?

MR. KNIGHTLEY (*shakes his head*). You have got it wrong as usual, dearest Emma. Mr. Robert Martin is the man. He is desperately in love and means to marry her.

EMMA. Mr. Robert Martin is very obliging, but is he sure that Harriet means to marry him?

MR. KNIGHTLEY. He came to see me at Donwell Abbey last evening to consult me about it. I had no hesitation in advising him to marry. I praised the fair lady too, and altogether sent him away very happy.

EMMA (*smiling at him*). Pray, Mr. Knightley, how do you know that Mr. Martin has not proposed already?

MR. KNIGHTLEY. I can readily believe it; he is so very much in love, I can imagine he would not waste much time.

EMMA. Mr. Martin has proposed *by letter*, sir, and is to be refused.

MR. KNIGHTLEY (*at once angry, stands up*). Refused! Then Harriet Smith is a greater simpleton than I had believed her.

EMMA. Oh to be sure, it is always incomprehensible to a man that a woman should ever refuse an offer of marriage.

MR. KNIGHTLEY. Emma! this is your doing; you persuaded her to refuse him.

EMMA (*rises*). And if I did, which I am far from allowing, I should not feel I had done wrong. I cannot admit him to be Harriet's equal.

MR. KNIGHTLEY. No, he is not her equal, indeed, for he is as much her superior in sense as in situation.

EMMA. You are a very warm friend to Mr. Martin, but most unjust to Harriet.

EMMA *crosses to* D.C. — *then walks up and down angrily.*

MR. KNIGHTLEY. And you have been no friend to Harriet.

EMMA. Since Harriet has been visiting at Hartfield she knows what gentlemen are. Mr. Martin's manners leave much to be desired.

MR. KNIGHTLEY. Nonsense, arrant nonsense. Robert Martin's manners have sense, sincerity and good-humour to recommend them, and his mind has more true gentility than Harriet Smith could ever understand.

EMMA (*quickly changing her tactics, and wandering over to the window*). How this unexpected sunshine makes one long to see the spring.

MR. KNIGHTLEY. As a friend, let me give you a hint. If Mr. Elton is the man you have chosen, I think you have laboured in vain.

EMMA. How so?

MR. KNIGHTLEY. Mr. Elton may talk sentimentally, but he will act rationally. He is very ambitious when he talks of young ladies and the possibility of marriage. Take my word for it, Elton is much more likely to have designs on an heiress like yourself than on Harriet Smith.

EMMA (D.R.). Complete and utter nonsense. I am very much obliged to you, sir, for the hint; when a young man is as deeply in love as Mr. Elton is, he sometimes forgets to act rationally; besides he knows his station and would not presume to ask for Emma Woodhouse.

MR. KNIGHTLEY. You will live to regret this day's foolishness, Emma. I beg of you, use your influence to further Robert Martin's suit before real damage is done.

EMMA. And undo all the good work I have achieved? I am sorry, sir, but that would not be possible.

MR. KNIGHTLEY (*exasperated*). Then I wish you a very good day.

He bows and goes out. When he has gone EMMA *crosses to the desk again and speaks her thoughts aloud.*

EMMA. What does Mr. Knightley know of love? Though I wish he had not planted this seed of doubt as regards Mr. Elton. I wish that what Mr. Knightley says would not always have such a ring of maddening conviction. (*Picks up letter.*) I will not allow him to undermine my confidence in this way. Mr. Elton is in love, those sighs alone are proof of it. Oh, fiddle-dee-dee to Mr. Knightley.

Enter SERLE, MISS BATES *close behind him.*

SERLE. Miss Bates to see you, ma'am.

EMMA. Miss Bates. . . . (*Crosses from desk to* U.C.)

MISS BATES *is a middle-aged spinster with an eager, bird-like appearance. She radiates kindliness and goodwill. Words seem to pour from her whenever she opens her mouth.*

MISS BATES. Oh, my dear Miss Woodhouse, I positively had to call and thank you. I am really quite overpowered. Such a beautiful hind-quarter of pork as you sent. You are too bountiful. . . .

EMMA. You are more than welcome, dear Miss Bates. Pray be seated.

EMMA *puts* MISS BATES *across to sit in armchair.* EMMA C.

MISS BATES. Yes indeed, thank you, Miss Woodhouse, so very kind. If there is one thing I love better than another it is pork — a roast loin of pork. You may imagine the pleasure that my dear Jane should arrive in time to share it — three months she is to be with us — three months at least.

EMMA. Miss Fairfax is here in Highbury?

MISS BATES. Such a pleasure it was. I have not yet recovered from it. Such an abundance of news I do not know where to begin. I trust I am the first to tell you of Mr. Churchill's arrival. You may guess what a flurry it has thrown me in.

EMMA. Mr. Frank Churchill?

MISS BATES (*nods*). Mr. *Weston's* son.

EMMA. Mr. Churchill has come to visit his father at last. This is news indeed.

MISS BATES. You are too obliging. I said to myself, dear Miss Woodhouse must be acquainted with everything. . . .

EMMA. When did the gentleman arrive?

MISS BATES (*rises*). Mr. Weston met him off the coach at the Crown. Such a dear surprise for Mrs. Weston. Imagine, Miss Woodhouse, how pleasant a surprise for her . . .

EMMA. Hardly a surprise, Miss Bates. Mr. Churchill was expected for his father's wedding.

MISS BATES. As you say, Miss Woodhouse, no surprise at all. I am told — mind you I do not know how true it is, but I am told it is all the fault of his aunt, Mrs. Churchill of Enscombe.

EMMA. Mr. and Mrs. Weston were greatly upset he could not attend their wedding.

MISS BATES. She is so very possessive of his affections; they say she will not allow him to marry during her lifetime.

EMMA. Indeed.

MISS BATES. As you say, Miss Woodhouse, *indeed!* When the first Mrs. Weston died, before you were born, so you will not remember, the Churchills made Frank their heir — a noble gesture . . .

EMMA. Yes, Miss Bates, I have heard that history, a score of times. . . . (*Crosses to below sofa —* MISS BATES *follows.*)

MISS BATES. The condition was that he should be called by the family name of . . . of . . .

EMMA. Churchill. (*Sits on sofa.*)

MISS BATES (*sits on sofa*). You are too obliging, dear Miss Woodhouse. There I was in the haberdasher's with dear Jane to buy some ribbed elastic . . . a yard I think it was . . . then I stopped to have a word with a nodding acquaintance when I caught sight of Mrs. Weston outside the Crown . . . so I thought if I hurry . . . I might kill two birds with a single visit and tell you of Jane and Mr.

Churchill's arrival in the same breath . . .

EMMA. As indeed you have, Miss Bates.

MISS BATES. Merely to save Mrs. Weston the trouble of telling you herself. For no other reason, I assure you, Miss Woodhouse.

EMMA. You are all kindness, ma'am.

Enter SERLE.

SERLE. Mrs. Weston.

EMMA (*rises*). Mrs. Weston — oh, show her in, Serle.

MISS BATES (*crestfallen*). Oh, Mrs. Weston, and I have not had time to tell you everything myself. . . . (*Rises.*)

SERLE *bows and goes out.* MISS BATES *drops bag* R. *of sofa, picks it up, crosses above sofa to* C. MRS. WESTON *comes in. She does not see* MISS BATES.

MRS. WESTON. Emma, my love.

EMMA. How good it is to see you. (*They embrace.*)

MRS. WESTON. I have such news.

MISS BATES. Here I am, Mrs. Weston.

MRS. WESTON (*crestfallen*). Oh, Miss Bates, an unexpected pleasure. (*It is obviously an unexpected disappointment.*)

EMMA. Pray be seated. (MRS. WESTON *and* EMMA *walk to the settee arm in arm. They sit,* EMMA C., MRS. WESTON R.)

MISS BATES. As I was saying to Miss Woodhouse, such a dear surprise, Mrs. Weston. (*Moves to settee, sits* L. *of* EMMA *who is imprisoned between them.*) Imagine, dear Miss Woodhouse . . .

MRS. WESTON (*simultaneously*). Oh, Emma, my love . . .

They smile at each other apologetically.

MISS BATES (*magnanimously*). Pray continue, dear Mrs. Weston.

MRS. WESTON. You are all kindness, ma'am. Oh, Emma, he is quite the young man one would choose for a son. You may imagine . . .

MISS BATES. Imagine the pleasure, Mrs. Weston. (*Leans in front of* EMMA.) Three months she is to be with us. Three months at least. . . .

EMMA *enjoys the situation and turns her head from one to the other.*

MRS. WESTON. Frank is to be here for three months also.

EMMA. How has he managed to break from Mrs. Churchill's leash at last?

MRS. WESTON. The lady has moved to Richmond for the time being. Some new treatment is the reason given. . . .

MISS BATES. So many treatments as there always are for everything.

EMMA. What sort of a young gentleman is Mr. Churchill?

MRS. WESTON *opens her mouth to speak, but* MISS BATES *has forestalled her.*

MISS BATES. Upon my word he is fortune's favourite, nothing wanting . . . he has position . . .

MRS. WESTON. Wealth . . .

EMMA'*s head goes from one to the other.*

MISS BATES. Pleasant manners . . .

MRS. WESTON. And a ready wit . . .

MISS BATES. That is what they say . . .

EMMA. There must be a flaw somewhere. His looks at least must be below average?

MISS BATES. No indeed, Miss Woodhouse, *above*! He is so handsome I have never seen the like.

EMMA. Where is the gentleman now, madam? I cannot wait to see him.

MRS. WESTON. I left him at the Crown with Mr. Weston; he is to join me here directly.

EMMA. I am all excitement . . .

MISS BATES (*raises her hands in horror*). Oh, such a dreadful thing!

EMMA (*concerned*). What is it, Miss Bates?

MISS BATES. I have left my dear Jane at the haberdasher's. . . . (*Rises.*) I must go to her at once.

EMMA (*rises*). Yes, indeed, Miss Bates. Pray bring Miss Fairfax to see us, sometime when you are passing.

MISS BATES. At once, Miss Woodhouse! I shall fetch my dear Jane at once. Pray do not disturb yourselves, it will take me but a moment. Such an agreeable visit . . . thank you so much. (MISS BATES *goes out. There is a smile of understanding between* MRS. WESTON *and* EMMA.)

EMMA. Why did Miss Fairfax have to arrive at the same time as Mr. Churchill? How true it is when they say that all our joys are touched with pain.

MRS. WESTON. (*Smiling, rises and crosses to* EMMA *at fire.*) You are not over-fond of dear Jane, are you, my love?

EMMA. There is nothing I have against her — but that she is so very reserved, so very nice and so correct.

MRS. WESTON. Well, I should not be surprised if the lady were to make an excellent match.

EMMA (*excited at once, pulls footstool forward and sits* L. *of* MRS. WESTON). Have you heard a rumour concerning her?

MRS. WESTON. It would not surprise me in the

least if Mr. Knightley were to propose.

EMMA. Mr. Knightley and Jane Fairfax! Dear Mrs. Weston, how could you think of such a thing?

MRS. WESTON. He is never done singing her praises. You know he has frequently held her up as an example to you, Emma.

EMMA. Surely that is no reason why he must marry her.

MRS. WESTON. He has given her the use of his carriage to make calls. I am sure there is something in it.

EMMA. Mr. Knightley to marry, it is not possible. I cannot believe it. Besides, it will not do. My nephew, little Henry Knightley, is the heir to Donwell Abbey. If Mr. Knightley were to marry and have children, little Henry would be cut out.

MRS. WESTON. But if Mr. Knightley really wished to marry, you would not have him refrain on little Henry's account. A boy of six years old who knows nothing of the matter.

EMMA. Yes, I would. I could not bear to have Henry supplanted. Such a marriage would be most unsuitable.

MRS. WESTON. I believe Jane Fairfax would make him an excellent wife.

EMMA. But Mr. Knightley does not want to marry, and if you please, do not put such an idea into his head. He is as happy as possible by himself. He has his sheep and his library, and he is extremely fond of his brother's children, particularly little Henry.

SERLE *comes in.*

SERLE. Mr. Frank Churchill.

EMMA. Send him in at once, Serle.

SERLE *bows and goes out. The ladies rise, smoothe their hair, pat their dresses, etc.*

MRS. WESTON. I do hope you will take to Frank, dearest Emma. He is so very engaging a young man.

EMMA. Have we not always been at one? If you approve of him how can I help but like him?

Well satisfied, MRS. WESTON *smiles contentedly.* FRANK CHURCHILL *comes in. He is all* MRS. WESTON *has said he is, and about twenty-five years old.*

MRS. WESTON. Frank, this is my Emma.

EMMA *bobs,* FRANK *bends over her hand.*

EMMA. I am delighted to make your acquaintance, sir, and bid you welcome to Hartfield.

MRS. WESTON *moves* D.R.

FRANK. Mrs. Weston has said so much about Hartfield and its charming hostess, I confess I feel at home already.

EMMA (*charmed by him*). Pray do, sir, we are honoured; and do be seated. Can I offer you some refreshment?

FRANK. We have had more than enough refreshment at the Crown, Miss Woodhouse. Do not tempt me to any more, I beg of you.

MRS. WESTON. Where is your father gone, Frank?

FRANK. I left him with Mr. Elton at the Crown, madam.

Enter SERLE *followed by* MISS BATES *and* MISS FAIRFAX. JANE FAIRFAX *is about twenty-one years old. Her dark beauty is classic in design. As* EMMA *has said, her manner is very correct and reserved.*

SERLE. Miss Bates, Miss Fairfax.

MISS BATES. Here is my dear Jane, Miss Woodhouse. We have but three minutes, not a moment longer.

EMMA. Welcome back to Highbury, Miss Fairfax.

JANE. You are all kindness, Miss Woodhouse.

EMMA. May I present Mr. Churchill, Miss Bates, Miss Fairfax.

JANE *is silent as she shakes hands.*

MISS BATES. Oh, but we are acquainted. Mr. Churchill has already called to visit us.

This remark has the effect of making everyone in the room stare wide-eyed with surprise.

MRS. WESTON. I did not realise that you were a friend of Miss Bates, Frank?

FRANK. I called on Miss Fairfax, madam. We had a short acquaintance at Weymouth. Miss Fairfax' guardians and my aunt were friends.

MISS BATES. We had but finished luncheon when Mr. Churchill arrived. So tender was the pork. It was Miss Woodhouse who was so kind as to send us the hind-quarter of pork, Jane dear, so very kind.

JANE (*looking miserably unhappy*). More than kind, dear Miss Woodhouse.

MISS BATES. Never is a porker killed at Hartfield, Mr. Churchill, but we always get the hind-quarter. Where is dear Mr. Woodhouse? We had thought to see him. He is so fond of my dear Jane.

EMMA. Papa has gone for his daily exercise. He will be all disappointment if you must leave before he returns.

MRS. WESTON. Well, Frank, what do you think of Highbury on seeing it for the first time?

FRANK. I confess I am quite delighted with the village and the neighbourhood. I think I have never been happier in my life than at this moment of returning home. I have been away far too long.

MRS. WESTON. Charming, Frank. You could not put a nicer compliment to us all.

FRANK. Tell me, Miss Woodhouse, have you a musical society here in Highbury?

MRS. WESTON. My dear Emma is one of our foremost performers.

FRANK. Then Highbury is fortunate indeed. I have already had a sample of its talent.

EMMA. How so, pray?

FRANK. Miss Fairfax did us the honour of performing one evening at Weymouth. All who heard her were loud in their praise.

EMMA. Miss Fairfax is indeed an excellent performer and far superior to myself.

JANE. I cannot allow that, Miss Woodhouse.

FRANK (*crosses to above piano*). Then let us put it to the test. Here is the instrument. You shall both perform.

JANE. I beg of you to forgive me, not to-day if you please. I do not feel up to it.

FRANK (*concerned*). You are not ill, Miss Fairfax; I trust that you are not ill.

JANE. No, not ill, sir. Really it is nothing at all.

MISS BATES. Jane has caught a slight cold — one of Jane's colds, you know — I think the journey must have been too much for her.

FRANK. Then, Miss Woodhouse, *you* must oblige, you cannot claim illness as an excuse. I confess I have never seen such a picture of radiant health as you are.

EMMA. You make me feel like the country bumpkin I am, sir.

FRANK. But you will perform?

EMMA. As your hostess, I can refuse you nothing of hospitality. (*Crosses to piano and sits* R. *of* FRANK.)

MRS. WESTON. You must not forget, Frank, it was I who taught Emma to perform. Any shortcomings you may find must be blamed on me. (*Sits* D.R. *armchair*.)

FRANK (*bows to* MRS. WESTON *and smiles. At piano*). What shall it be? (*Looks through bundle of music.*) " Robin Adair "? Even I who know nothing of music know " Robin Adair ".

EMMA (*seating herself*). Then let us perform together, sir?

JANE. Mr. Churchill sings delightfully. (*Sits* U.L. *armchair*.)

MISS BATES. There is nothing I love more than a duet. Do not they make a handsome pair, Mrs. Weston? A very handsome pair indeed. (*Sits sofa*.)

EMMA *strikes the opening bars and starts to sing.* FRANK *joins her. They sing charmingly together. When they have finished the small audience is loud in its praise.*

MRS. WESTON. Perfectly charming. You did not disgrace me, my Emma.

FRANK. Miss Woodhouse performs delightfully. Her style and taste are perfection.

JANE. Their voices match wonderfully well, do they not, aunt?

MISS BATES. A very well-matched pair indeed.

MRS. WESTON. And now, Frank, we must be on our way. Look what time it is already.

FRANK. With your permission, Miss Woodhouse, I shall call again to-morrow. Mrs. Weston did not over-praise the charm of a visit to Hartfield. I have enjoyed myself extremely.

JANE. We must also take our leave.

MISS BATES. Yes, indeed, we must be running. Have you forgotten your muff, Jane dear?

JANE. No, aunt.

EMMA. Dear Papa will be broken-hearted to have missed your visit.

MISS BATES. You are too kind to be sure. Such a delightful visit! Pray remember us to dear Mr. Woodhouse. He is so fond of dear Jane. So very kind. Give him our thanks for the hind-quarter. How blessed we are in our neighbours. So very bountiful.

EMMA. Pray come again soon, Miss Fairfax, Miss Bates.

As they move towards the door SERLE *ushers in* MR. ELTON.

MRS. WESTON. Oh, Mr. Elton, just in time to meet my stepson, Mr. Frank Churchill. Mr. Elton is our new Vicar in Highbury.

MR. ELTON. I have already had the honour of Mr. Churchill's acquaintance, madam. (*Bows to* MISS FAIRFAX *and* MISS BATES.)

FRANK (*bows*). Sir.

The ladies curtsey. They all go towards the double doors.

EMMA. Pray come again soon, one and all.

MISS BATES (*as she goes out*). Wrap yourself well, Jane dear, and see that you do not catch cold. You know how it always is after a room is too warm.

MRS. WESTON (*kissing her*). And you must come and visit us without delay, dearest Emma.

They smile. MR. CHURCHILL *bows gallantly.* MR. ELTON *follows suit. They go out.*

MR. ELTON (*to* R. *of sofa. As soon as the door is closed*). Such charming company as one always meets at Hartfield — so distinguished, so exactly so.

EMMA (*somewhat dreamily*). Yes, Mr. Churchill is a very fine sort of young man, is he not?

MR. ELTON. Mr. Weston would have me drink again and again to the health of his distinguished son, so happy is he for his return.

EMMA. Mr. Churchill is all a father could wish for. He seems so very good-natured, so quick, so full of charm and easy manners. He leaves such an atmosphere of goodwill behind him. (*Sits sofa.*)

MR. ELTON. Mr. Churchill seems to have made a most favourable impression. We eligible bachelors will have our noses put out of joint before long.

ELTON *moves above sofa to* L. *of it.*

EMMA (*full of charm*). You are quite safe, dear Mr. Elton, you have nothing to fear. (*Holds out her hand affectionately.*)

MR. ELTON (*at once on his knees beside her, clutching her hand*). Oh, beloved Miss Woodhouse, this is the opportunity I have hoped and prayed for. I feared it would never come. So long I have adored you, so ardent is my attachment. I am ready to die should my love be unrequited. Tell me, beloved Miss Woodhouse, am I to live or die?

EMMA *has been too astonished to speak throughout this declaration.*

EMMA (*rises*). I am very much astonished, Mr. Elton. I fear you have been drinking too much of Mr. Weston's good wine. This to *me*. You forget yourself. You take me for my friend. Any message to Miss Smith I shall be most happy to deliver, but if you please, no more of this to me.

MR. ELTON (*rises*). Miss Smith! Message to Miss Smith? What can you possibly mean, dear lady?

EMMA. Mr. Elton, my astonishment is beyond anything I can express. After such behaviour as I witnessed to Miss Smith so short a time ago.

MR. ELTON. But I have never thought of Miss Smith in the whole course of my existence but as your friend. Oh, Miss Woodhouse, who can think of Miss Smith when Miss Woodhouse is near.

EMMA (*moving round above sofa to* C. — ELTON *following*). Sir, I have been in a most complete error of your views until this moment. Your seeming attachment to Miss Smith gave me great pleasure, but had I supposed she were not your attraction to Hartfield I should certainly have thought ill of your frequent visits.

MR. ELTON. I wish Miss Smith extremely well, and no doubt there are men who might not object to — shall we say — to the obscurity of her connections. Everybody has their level. For myself, I am not, I think, so much at a loss. No, madam, my visits to Hartfield have been for yourself only, and the encouragement I have received, the unmistakable encouragement——

EMMA. Encouragement! How dare you, sir! You have been entirely mistaken in supposing it. For myself I have no thought of matrimony, and I hope your disappointment will not be lasting, but as you remind me, everybody has their level, and no doubt you will find consolation in yours. Now, sir, I wish you a very good day.

Holds out her hand, which he ignores. He bows with great dignity, goes towards the door, and stops to speak.

MR. ELTON. I shall now take my leave of you; you are too proud, madam, too proud not to be humbled yet. To-morrow I shall make my departure for Bath where there are ladies who do not rate me at so low a level. Ladies of equal rank and fortune as yourself, madam.

EMMA. Perhaps equal in rank and fortune, sir, but surely not equal in taste.

MR. ELTON (*practically speechless with rage*). Good day to you, madam.

EMMA *curtseys to the ground. When she rises he has gone, and she is laughing to herself. But as she raises her head she catches sight of the portrait.*

EMMA (*sobering in a moment*). Oh, Harriet, my poor dear Harriet.

The Curtain falls

ACT II

SCENE I: *Morning in Spring*

The same about a month later. JANE FAIRFAX *is discovered sitting* D.R. *She crosses to the fire, looking expectantly towards the hall door. Presently* FRANK CHURCHILL *comes in, he closes the door behind him carefully. Then he swings round to face* JANE. *They move towards each other and meet centre stage.*

FRANK (*happily*). At last, dearest Jane, we have contrived to be alone at last.

JANE. This is madness, sir, utter madness.

FRANK (*immediately deflated*). I do not care. I am distracted beyond caring.

JANE. Everything will be undone if we are indiscreet now, sir. It will not do. (*Moves to pass him.*) I shall join the others before we are discovered.

FRANK (*in her way*). You need not be in such haste. I have to talk with you.

JANE. I beg of you to practise caution, and remember we are not in Weymouth now, sir.

FRANK. Would to God we were. There everything seemed possible. Now it is hopeless, utterly hopeless.

JANE (*with real feeling*). I implore you do not be so downcast. It could not be otherwise here in Highbury where we are both known. Surely you have realised that.

FRANK. I detest this place where every movement,

every glance is remarked upon. (*Moves towards her.*) Never have I known such misery. (*Tries to take her in his arms.*) Jane——

JANE. No, sir, I beg of you, do not come nearer — do not compromise me.

FRANK (*crosses* D.L. *to desk*). We should never have come here.

JANE. What else was there we could do? Do not give in so easily, and let us try to practise patience. After this folly we must now be doubly careful.

FRANK. And doubly deceitful, doubly cruel?

JANE. Understand me, sir, I beg of you, merely in the name of necessity.

FRANK (*bitterly*). Shall I also increase my efforts of deception? Shall I increase my overtures to the lady?

JANE (*quietly*). You must do as you think fit, sir.

FRANK (*starting to laugh*). If it were not all so damnably serious it might be tolerably amusing. If only one were not so absolutely helpless. (*He clenches his fists to control himself.*)

MR. *and* MRS. WESTON *come in with* MR. KNIGHTLEY. MR. WESTON *is a pleasant-looking gentleman farmer, devoted to his wife and extremely proud of his son.*

MRS. WESTON (*to* C.). Ah, there you are, Frank. (*Surprised.*) And you too, Miss Fairfax.

MR. WESTON. Miss Woodhouse was looking for you, Frank. There is a suggestion to turn the dining-room at the Crown into a ballroom. They want your advice.

MRS. WESTON. 'Pon my soul, Miss Fairfax, you look quite flushed, do you feel quite well? I trust you have not caught cold again.

JANE. There is nothing the matter with me, madam. I assure you I am quite well.

MR. WESTON (*bluff and hearty, teasing her*). What has my rogue of a son been saying to make you blush, Miss Fairfax, what has he been saying? (*Points his fingers at* JANE *in mock accusation.*)

JANE (*embarrassed*). Saying? Nothing at all, sir, I assure you; what should he be saying?

FRANK. My father is teasing you, Miss Fairfax; pay no attention to him. We have merely been laughing at some ridiculous woman, sir, a mutual acquaintance at Weymouth.

MRS. WESTON. One forgets you had a previous meeting.

MR. KNIGHTLEY (D.R., *who has been looking on interestedly*). Quite a remarkable coincidence that you should both have a home in Highbury and discover it on a casual meeting.

MRS. WESTON. You must have been thrown in each other's society considerably.

MR. KNIGHTLEY. Your two parties joined up, did they not?

FRANK. You know how it is at watering-places, and lovely as it is, Weymouth is no exception.

MR. WESTON. Yes, yes, it is always the same at watering-places. I remember once when . . .

FRANK (*breaking in on him*). Forgive me, sir, had I not better join Miss Woodhouse to complete the arrangements for the ball?

MRS. WESTON. Yes, Frank, do, or we shall all be exhausted with journeys between here and the Crown for the rest of the day.

FRANK. Then if you will excuse me, ladies.

He bows and goes out.

MR. WESTON (*crosses* D.R.). It is such a long time since we had a ball in Highbury. I confess to be quite excited about it.

MRS. WESTON. If only Randalls had a ballroom, there need not be all these arrangements at the Crown.

MR. KNIGHTLEY (*crosses to* C.). The ball was Emma's idea, was it not?

MRS. WESTON. No, I believe it was Frank who first suggested it.

MR. KNIGHTLEY. Emma is already too much inclined to frivolity to need encouragement.

MRS. WESTON. Indeed, Mr. Knightley, you are grown old before your time. Why should they not have a ball? Why should they not enjoy every moment of their youth?

MR. WESTON. Such a handsome pair they will make in a ballroom, so gay, so full of life as they both are, so very well suited.

MRS. WESTON. Never were two people better suited. It is the secret wish of Mr. Weston and myself that something will come of it, so very well matched as they are.

JANE *walks towards double doors to hide her distress.*

MR. KNIGHTLEY. I cannot agree, dear Mrs. Weston. They are far too much alike.

MRS. WESTON. But they get on so wonderfully well together — they pursue the same interests.

MR. KNIGHTLEY. Such as this present arrangement for the ball?

MRS. WESTON. And more besides. Both have privately hinted to me, if not of an attachment, certainly of the warmest feelings of friendship.

JANE (*moving towards the door, very agitatedly*). I had better go and find my aunt. She will be wondering what has happened to me.

MR. WESTON. Then I shall accompany you. I am still old-fashioned enough to disapprove of a young lady walking out of doors without an escort.

JANE. You are more than kind, sir, but I assure you it is not necessary. The Crown is but a minute's walk from the gate.

MR. WESTON (*opening the door*). I insist, Miss Fairfax, I positively insist.

JANE. Very well, sir.

MR. WESTON. I shall be but a moment, my love.

MRS. WESTON (*rises*). Do not be longer, sir, it is time we returned to Randalls.

MR. WESTON. Yes, my love.

JANE *and* MR. WESTON *go out.*

MRS. WESTON (*looking after him*). Oh, what a fortunate woman I am, Mr. Knightley. I could not have a better husband. I wish that everyone could have the happiness I have.

MR. KNIGHTLEY. You are both fortunate indeed. The perfect mate is more difficult to find than the rarest jewel in the world.

MRS. WESTON (*crosses to sit sofa*). Oh, I should not say that. What of Mr. Elton and his bride, they seem delighted with each other and they have not looked far.

MR. KNIGHTLEY. You forget, Mrs. Weston, they have been married but a few days. You could not call that a fair test of friendship, let alone of marriage.

MRS. WESTON. Emma has been particularly quiet on the matter. She has not even mentioned the bride. I cannot understand it.

MR. KNIGHTLEY (*crosses to sit sofa*). Do you know if she has told Miss Smith of Elton's marriage yet? The news must have been a considerable surprise to Emma, but it will be a decided shock to Miss Smith.

MRS. WESTON. You know Emma always puts off the things that are unpleasant until the last moment. It has not been necessary with Miss Smith confined to her room this last week or so.

MR. KNIGHTLEY. And now that she has gone out to-day for the first time someone is bound to tell her.

MRS. WESTON. Poor child.

MR. KNIGHTLEY. Is her throat completely recovered? Has the fever entirely gone?

MRS. WESTON. Oh yes, some days since. (*Confidentially*) It is my private opinion that Emma might have encouraged Harriet to stay in her room longer than was necessary.

MR. KNIGHTLEY. Because she is ashamed of the mischief she has done. Miss Smith would never have considered Elton as a suitor if Emma had not put the nonsense into her head.

MRS. WESTON. We have no proof of that, sir. Miss Smith seems to fall in and out of love with the aptitude of a Jack-in-the-box.

MR. KNIGHTLEY (*rises, crosses* L.C.). In my opinion, Jane Fairfax would have made Emma an infinitely more suitable companion. Her mind is cultured, she is reserved, ladylike and accomplished.

MRS. WESTON. More accomplished than Emma, in fact. Do you imagine Emma would want Jane Fairfax being superior in everything wherever they go?

MR. KNIGHTLEY (*laughing*). Indeed I cannot

imagine it, but it would do Emma a world of good. It is exactly what she needs.

EMMA *and* MR. WOODHOUSE *come in.* EMMA *is in a petulant mood.*

MRS. WESTON. Well, Emma, is it decided? Where is the ball to take place? At Randalls? Or at the Crown Inn?

MR. WOODHOUSE. No, Mrs. Weston, it is not decided; your house is too small and the dancers will be too hot and catch cold. The Crown Inn is too large and they will not be hot enough, and they will still catch cold.

MRS. WESTON. Is this your opinion as well, Emma?

EMMA. I should not dare to give an opinion against so much opposition and disapproval.

MRS. WESTON. And where is Frank? What does he say?

EMMA. He is all enthusiasm for the Crown, where it will be possible to have a larger company.

MR. WOODHOUSE. That young man does not think of the draught. He is very much inclined to open doors and leave them open. I do not mean to set you against him, but if you ask me he is not quite the thing. (*He crosses, sits armchair.*)

MRS. WESTON. Oh come, sir. I am sure he does not mean to be inconsiderate. If you are so against the Crown, then we shall settle immediately on Randalls.

EMMA (*crosses* D.R.). What could be worse than dancing without space to turn in, and such a small company too. Even if we were to open the windows it would still be too hot.

MR. WOODHOUSE. Open the windows! I never heard of such a thing. Dancing with the windows open! Is it the influence of Mr. Churchill that makes you so selfish all of a sudden, Emma?

EMMA (*crossing* C., *her temper rising*). No indeed, Papa. It is my own selfishness entirely, and so much disapproval of an innocent enjoyment, gives me pleasure in it.

MR. WOODHOUSE (*fearful of* EMMA'S *temper*). Now, now, my dearest Emma, you know I would not thwart your pleasure for the world. It is only my fear of your health and the health of all your good friends that bids me caution you.

MR. KNIGHTLEY. So much trouble for a few hours' enjoyment hardly seems worth while.

EMMA (*turning on him*). Indeed, sir, the trouble is half the enjoyment. I find myself in excellent spirits.

MISS FAIRFAX, MR. CHURCHILL *and* MR. WESTON *come in*.

JANE. My aunt has stopped to speak with Mrs. Coles. She will be here directly. (*She crosses* D.R.)

Gipsy music is heard in the distance.

MRS. WESTON. Listen, Emma, the music.

All listen.

EMMA (*crosses* C. *Brightening*). This is delightful. What can it be? A circus?

FRANK. Merely a band of gipsies. We saw them but a moment ago.

MR. WOODHOUSE. Gipsies. Gipsies in Highbury. I do not like it, Emma, I do not like it at all.

FRANK. You need not worry, sir, they seemed to be passing through the town.

EMMA. Indeed. I am sorry to have missed them. So romantic and carefree as they can be.

MR. WOODHOUSE. Rolling stones . . . that is what they are. . . . Rolling stones. . . .

MR. WESTON. Come, sir, gipsies are harmless enough. They are said to be thieves, but I do not believe it. No gipsy has ever stolen from me.

MR. WOODHOUSE. As long as they are passing through. That is all I care about. (*Sits armchair.*)

The music fades.

FRANK (*to* MRS. WESTON). What has been decided about the ball, madam?

EMMA. Nothing at all, sir.

MRS. WESTON. If only Randalls were twice as big. If we had but one room the size of any of your rooms, Mr. Woodhouse, the difficulty would be overcome.

FRANK *and* EMMA *look at each other instantly, struck by the same idea.*

EMMA (*happily*). Why did we not think of it before? Of course we must give the ball here at Hartfield. Is not that an excellent idea, Papa?

MR. WOODHOUSE. Think of the upheaval, my dear, think of it. At least we are free of draughts here, but think of the upheaval.

EMMA (*planning, and in her element*). The inner hall will make a perfect ballroom. The dining-room leading straight off it is so very convenient for supper. The library can be laid out for cards and this drawing-room for sitting-out and conversation.

FRANK. Dear Miss Woodhouse, you have a genius for organisation.

EMMA. I have a genius for stupidity or I should have thought of it hours ago.

MRS. WESTON (*to* MR. WOODHOUSE). What is your opinion of this scheme, sir?

MR. WOODHOUSE. I have no complaint to make. It shall be as Emma wishes.

EMMA *kisses him, he pats her hand.*

MR. KNIGHTLEY. As indeed it always is, sir.

EMMA *gives him a look.* MISS BATES *comes fluttering in excitedly.*

MISS BATES (*to* MR. WOODHOUSE). Oh, my dear sir, such news about Mr. Elton.

EMMA. What news?

MISS BATES. Well, we called on them this morning — so very elegant as she is — and an heiress too. They arrived in their own carriage driven all the way from Bath. A Miss Hawkins. So very well connected. A fortune of ten thousand pounds to her credit. Mr. Elton is the happiest man in the world.

MR. WOODHOUSE. Mr. Elton seemed to me to be very well off as he was.

MISS BATES. A new neighbour for us all. I love a romance above all things.

EMMA (*crosses to and sits sofa,* L. *of* MRS. WESTON). It must indeed have been a romance, quite love at first sight to have met, courted, the banns put up and married all in four weeks.

MR. KNIGHTLEY (*crossing to* EMMA). I told you, did I not, that Mr. Elton was a young man of considerable enterprise?

EMMA. I have not forgotten what you told me, sir.

MISS BATES. One had rather fancied it might be some young lady hereabouts. Mrs. Goddard whispered to me — well, never mind. How is dear little Miss Smith? She seems quite recovered now. I wonder if she has heard the news?

EMMA (*on her mettle*). When Miss Smith does hear it, I can vouch that she will wish both Mr. and Mrs. Elton every possible happiness.

MISS BATES. To be sure. I knew Mrs. Goddard

had it wrong. Mrs. Goddard always gets a story wrong. (*She sits armchair.*)

FRANK (*crosses to* JANE, D.R.). What is your opinion of the bride, Miss Fairfax?

JANE. Mrs. Elton seems a lively sort of person, I cannot say more than that ; she was most willing to be friendly.

MR. KNIGHTLEY. I have invariably found that human nature is so well disposed towards persons in interesting situations, one has only either to be married or die to be kindly spoken of.

FRANK. You will soon be able to form your own opinion, Miss Woodhouse, when you make your formal call on the bride.

MR. KNIGHTLEY. What is your opinion of the bride, Emma?

EMMA (*surprised*). Mine, sir?

MISS BATES. Mrs. Elton is indeed a woman to be envied, to possess such a fortune and such a husband. (*Sighs.*) Would that my dear Papa had been rich rather than religious. Your dear Grandmama went to the Vicarage as a bride, Jane; how happy she must have been.

MR. WOODHOUSE. Excellent fellow, the Reverend Bates. So very quiet and reserved. Every inch a gentleman.

MISS BATES. Jane takes after him, not like me. I think I talk too much to take after Papa.

MR. WOODHOUSE. It was the Reverend Bates married me to your dear Mama, Emma, my love. How well I remember the day, all the bustle and upheaval as we set off to Weymouth for our honey-moon.

MISS BATES (*exclaims*). Weymouth! Oh sir, do

not mention the place. I cannot bear to hear it spoken of since dear Jane so nearly lose her life there.

JANE (*agitated, crossing to* MISS BATES). Aunt, if you please.

MISS BATES. If it had not been for you, dear Mr. Churchill, we should not have Jane with us now. So brave an act, so heroic.

MRS. WESTON. What is this, Frank?

EMMA. Why have we not heard of it before?

FRANK. It was nothing. A slight accident on a boating party, that is all.

MISS BATES. You saved her from drowning, sir, at peril to your own life. Jane has had a cold ever since. (*To* MR. WOODHOUSE) Do not mention Weymouth again, if you please; never shall I forget it.

MR. KNIGHTLEY. This is exceedingly modest of you, Churchill. I am surprised Miss Fairfax did not tell us herself, if only to sing your praises out of gratitude.

JANE. I am not wanting in gratitude, sir, that I do assure you.

FRANK. The blame is mine entirely. Realising how the story would upset my aunt, I asked Miss Fairfax to be silent on the matter. I begged her to show any gratitude she might feel by remaining silent. (*Coldly*) I understood she had done so.

JANE (*humiliated*). I have told no one other than my aunt. I did not think she would . . .

MISS BATES. Have I talked too much again, Jane dear? I am extremely sorry, but the mention of that place chills me to the marrow. So noble a rescue it was.

FRANK. Miss Bates has indeed as marked a talent as Miss Fairfax for the keeping of a secret.

EMMA. Surely you cannot accuse Miss Fairfax of indiscretion, Mr. Churchill. Indeed, when I hear the proverb " Still waters run deep ", I shall always think it should be " Still waters run deep as Miss Fairfax ".

JANE (*rises*). Thank you for supporting me, Miss Woodhouse.

MISS BATES. Now, my dear Jane, we positively must be running away.

EMMA. Must you go so soon?

MISS BATES. You are too obliging, my dear Miss Woodhouse, but we really must — a most agreeable visit — such interesting news. Good day, dear Mr. Woodhouse. Pray do not disturb yourself.

MR. WOODHOUSE. Thank you, Miss Bates.

MISS BATES. We shall have to look round by Mrs. Goddard's and Mrs. Perry's to see how they are to-day.

She goes out.

MRS. WESTON. We must also take our leave, my dearest Emma.

Exit MR. *and* MRS. WESTON.

FRANK. It seems we have used your house as a consulting-room. So many visits have there been between here and the Crown. I am most happy that our plans for the ball are so comfortably settled.

He holds her hand longer than he need. This is not lost on JANE FAIRFAX, *who leaves hurriedly.*

MISS BATES (*from the hall*). I'm waiting, Jane dear.

EMMA. I shall look forward to it, extremely, sir.

FRANK (*warmly*). Allow me now, dear lady, to claim the first dance, the last dance, and so many as you may spare me in between.

With much ceremony, good wishes returned, bows and curtseys, the guests take their leave, EMMA *and* MR. KNIGHTLEY *go to see them off. Only* MR. WOODHOUSE *is left in the room. The party has exhausted him. He settles comfortably in his chair, places his silk handkerchief over his face and goes to sleep.* EMMA *and* MR. KNIGHTLEY *come into the room and close the door. They speak quietly not to waken* MR. WOODHOUSE.

MR. KNIGHTLEY (D.C.). Emma, I am most sincerely sorry about the news of Elton. Miss Smith is bound to be distressed.

EMMA (D.R.). You have so little regard for my friend, I should have expected you to be glad, sir.

MR. KNIGHTLEY. That she is your friend alone, Emma, makes me sorry for her awkward situation, forgetting your part in the affair.

EMMA (*crosses* D.L.). It would seem the world is not charitable to those who suffer from the misfortune of obscurity at birth.

MR. KNIGHTLEY. Poverty at birth seems to me a greater misfortune than obscurity, and I have not noticed your being particularly charitable to Miss Fairfax, who is a charming and delightful young woman.

EMMA. Miss Fairfax is not as candid about her affairs as I prefer my friends to be. Why does she not return to her guardians?

MR. KNIGHTLEY. I understand that Colonel and Mrs. Campbell have gone to live in Ireland. Poor Miss Fairfax!

EMMA. I cannot see why she should excite your pity. Have not the Campbells lavished every affection on her. Indeed she has a wardrobe equal to my own.

MR. KNIGHTLEY. But think of her situation — she must now go out as a governess.

EMMA. As a governess! Oh! Even living in Ireland could not be worse than that.

MR. KNIGHTLEY. Come, Emma, where is your charity now?

EMMA. If she were to give the impression of needing sympathy I should be the very first to offer mine.

MR. KNIGHTLEY. I think Jane Fairfax is a charming and delightful young woman. I have always been surprised that you and she have never been on a closer kind of friendship.

EMMA (*watching him*). I know you think very highly of Miss Fairfax, sir.

MR. KNIGHTLEY. I have the greatest regard for the lady. She has so much to commend her.

EMMA. You speak warmly, sir. Are we also to expect a mistress at Donwell Abbey at last?

MR. KNIGHTLEY. Enough, Emma, I will not have you match-making for me. I dare say Miss Fairfax would not have me if I were to ask her.

EMMA. You are not vain, sir, I will say that for you.

MR. KNIGHTLEY. I promise to let you know when I decide to ask the lady of my choice, if indeed I ever do. (*Thoughtfully*) No, even Jane Fairfax has a fault. (*Crosses* D.R.)

EMMA (*crossing, sits sofa*). Tell me of it, sir, I am all eagerness.

MR. KNIGHTLEY. She has not the openness of temper I should wish for in a woman. No, Miss Fairfax will not do for me, I could not marry Miss Fairfax.

EMMA. I should say, sir, that you are so much occupied with the idea of *not* marrying her that I should not wonder if you were to end by doing so.

MR. KNIGHTLEY. While we are on the subject of Jane Fairfax, has it not occurred to you that she and Frank Churchill are employed in some mystery — there is something between them, I am convinced of it.

EMMA. Frank Churchill and Jane Fairfax! Nothing would be further from the truth. He has told me privately he does not admire the lady. Her coldness of manner, her pale beauty leave him quite without feeling.

MR. KNIGHTLEY (*sits sofa*). I could have sworn it. Those looks between them, the silence about the boating accident. Everything points to it.

EMMA. Utter nonsense, Mr. Knightley. But it is an amusing thought. (*Scoffing*) Miss Fairfax and Mr. Churchill. (*She laughs at him.*)

MR. KNIGHTLEY. Do not forget you may be as wrong about them as you were about Miss Smith and Mr. Elton.

EMMA. You are not prone to forgetting my errors, are you, sir?

MR. KNIGHTLEY. Have you told Miss Smith yet that Mr. Elton is married?

EMMA (*annoyed*). No, sir, I have not.

MR. KNIGHTLEY. I understand she has gone out to-day?

EMMA. She has.

MR. KNIGHTLEY. Knowing what the Highbury gossips are, you know someone is bound to tell her. Do you not think it is rather unkind to expose her to such a shock in public?

EMMA. I am aware of the possibility, sir. I had intended to tell her this morning but the opportunity did not present itself. I shall break the news the moment she returns. (*She is angry with him because she is angry with herself.*)

MR. KNIGHTLEY. I am glad to hear it. With all your faults I should never have accused you of cowardice.

EMMA (*rises and curtseys. Pertly*). I am obliged to you, sir, I'm sure.

MR. KNIGHTLEY. Emma, why did you pretend you had not met Mr. Elton's bride?

EMMA. I did not pretend anything of the kind, sir.

MR. KNIGHTLEY. You do not deny that you have called on the bride?

EMMA (*crosses* D.R.). No, sir, I do not deny it.

MR. KNIGHTLEY. So your curiosity could not be satisfied without seeing her for yourself.

EMMA. As the mistress of Hartfield it was my duty to call on the Vicar's wife. I have done no more than my duty.

HARRIET SMITH *bursts into the room in a state of great agitation.*

HARRIET. Oh, Miss Woodhouse, Miss Woodhouse, what do you think, the most dreadful thing. (*Seeing* MR. KNIGHTLEY) I beg your pardon, sir. (*She bobs —* MR. KNIGHTLEY *rises.*)

The stir of HARRIET'S *entrance has wakened* MR. WOODHOUSE.

MR. WOODHOUSE. What is it, what is it?

EMMA (*crosses to* MR. WOODHOUSE). Nothing, dearest Papa — you have been asleep, that is all.

MR. KNIGHTLEY (*affably*). Have you had a pleasant walk, Miss Smith?

HARRIET. Yes, sir, very pleasant indeed. (*She crosses to* U.R.)

MR. KNIGHTLEY. I am delighted to hear it.

MR. WOODHOUSE (*rising with difficulty*). If you will excuse me, my dear, I shall have Serle to get me half a glass of Madeira wine — just half a glass with water — that is all I take. (*To* MR. KNIGHTLEY) Will you join me, sir?

MR. KNIGHTLEY. Yes indeed, sir, then I must be on my way. Good-bye, Emma. I have enjoyed our talk extremely, and I trust you will have an equally enjoyable talk with Miss Smith.

EMMA (*with too brilliant a smile*). Rest assured, sir, I shall.

MR. KNIGHTLEY *returns the smile and bows.*

MR. KNIGHTLEY. Good day, Miss Smith.

HARRIET. A very good day to you, sir. (*Bobs.*)

MR. WOODHOUSE (*pats* HARRIET *as he passes her*). Pretty child. Noisy but pretty.

The gentlemen go out.

HARRIET (*going to* EMMA). Oh, Miss Woodhouse, what do you think has happened?

EMMA (*her arm round her*). Do not be upset, dearest Harriet. I understand your feelings.

HARRIET. It was quite by chance that I dropped into the haberdasher's to see if my spotted muslin had arrived while I had been ill. As I was waiting for Mrs. Ford to inquire about it the door opened and who do you think should walk in, Miss Woodhouse?

EMMA. Who it was does not matter, the fact is that you now know. If only I knew how to comfort you.

HARRIET. Oh, Miss Woodhouse, I felt miserable and my face must have been as white as my dress.

EMMA. Harriet, dearest, I shall think of some way to make you forget. It is all my fault. I admit it freely. If only I had talked with you this morning.

HARRIET. That could not have saved me from a surprise encounter, Miss Woodhouse.

EMMA (*astonished*). You mean you actually met them face to face?

SERLE *comes in.*

HARRIET. Yes, Miss Woodhouse, face to face.

EMMA. My poor Harriet, what a shock for you. What is it, Serle?

SERLE. Mr. and Mrs. Elton to see you, ma'am.

EMMA. Good heavens! They must have followed you here!

HARRIET. Mr. and Mrs. Elton? I do not understand.

EMMA (*crosses to* SERLE). Ask them to wait, Serle. Say you will look for me, but do not bring them here until I ring.

SERLE. Very good, ma'am.

He goes out.

HARRIET (*puzzled*). Mr. and Mrs. Elton. Has Mr. Elton brought his mother to see me, Miss Woodhouse?

EMMA. What is the matter with you, dearest Harriet, what can you be thinking of? Mr. Elton has brought his wife.

HARRIET. My Mr. Elton? . . .

EMMA. Yes, Harriet, your Mr. Elton.

HARRIET (*crosses to below sofa, followed by* EMMA). You are mistaken, Miss Woodhouse. We are not married yet. Mr. Elton has not even proposed. He has not even written since he has been away in Bath.

But now he has brought his mother to see me, all must be well.

EMMA. Good heavens, Harriet, have you gone out of your mind with the shock?

HARRIET. I do not think so, Miss Woodhouse. How does one know if one has gone out of one's mind? (*She feels her head.*)

EMMA. Do you not remember what you were told at the haberdasher's. Mr. Elton is married to another. A lady from Bath.

HARRIET (*she sinks on to sofa and lets out a scream*). Oh, Miss Woodhouse, no, it cannot be, it cannot be! This is too much of a shock. I cannot bear it! (*She screams again.*) I cannot bear it!

EMMA (*sits* L. *of* HARRIET). Be calm, Harriet, steady yourself. Listen to me. . . . Surely I cannot have been under a mistake?

HARRIET. I cannot bear it! I cannot bear it! (*Her arms and legs shaking.*)

EMMA. You mean to tell me you did not know they were married?

HARRIET. I do not know anything. Tell me Mr. Elton is not married to another, tell me that, Miss Woodhouse. (*She quietens down to wait for* EMMA'S *answer.*)

EMMA. Alas, Harriet, it is only too true. Mr. Elton returned while you were ill. I understood you knew.

HARRIET. It is too much for me to bear, Miss Woodhouse. (*Cries.*) Too much. What is there left of my faith when the Vicar himself can deceive me. (*Gulps back her tears.*)

EMMA (*impatient*). Enough of this. (*She crosses to the bell-pull, rings it briskly, then returns to* HARRIET, *grips her firmly.*) Harriet, here is a chance to prove how truly a lady you are. Put him to the shame he deserves. Here, take my smelling salts. Let your manner be quiet, composed and pleasant. Let him see what he has lost. Will you do that for my sake, Harriet?

HARRIET. Yes, Miss Woodhouse, but another shock so soon.

EMMA. Compose yourself, Harriet, I beg of you.

SERLE *comes in.*

SERLE. Mr. and Mrs. Elton.

HARRIET *rises and crosses* D.R.

EMMA (*going forward*). This is an honour, sir. (*The ladies curtsey.* MR. ELTON *bows.*) Delighted, madam.

MRS. ELTON. Delighted.

EMMA. Have you met Miss Smith? — Mrs. Elton.

They both curtsey. MRS. ELTON *is quite imposing on first appearance, but her voice is affected and her manner pretentious. She is completely self-assured. She bows coldly to* HARRIET. EMMA *bids them be seated.*

MRS. ELTON. Dear Miss Woodhouse, how nice it is to see you again, even for as short a visit as this must be.

EMMA. Thank you, madam. The pleasure is mutual.

MRS. ELTON. It is ever the same. So many people will be offended if they are not honoured by a visit on my first day calls.

EMMA. We do not easily take offence at Hartfield, madam.

MRS. ELTON. One has heard so much of the beauty of Hartfield. As soon as the carriage turned into the drive I said to Mr. E. (*indicates her husband*) how like it is to Maple Grove.

EMMA. Maple Grove?

MRS. ELTON. My brother, Mr. Suckling's seat near Bristol. The house too is alike. Only Maple Grove is so very large, but quite the same style. Even this room is the exact shape and size of the *morning* room at Maple Grove. I assure you, Miss Woodhouse, it makes one feel quite at home.

EMMA. To be sure.

MRS. ELTON. My brother and sister will be enchanted with this place. People who have extensive grounds themselves are always pleased when others have anything in the same style.

EMMA. Yes, madam, particularly when the grounds of others are smaller. When you have seen more of this neighbourhood I am afraid you will think you have over-valued the beauties of Hartfield. Surrey is full of beauties.

MRS. ELTON. Oh yes, I am aware of that. It is called the garden of England. Surrey is the garden of England, you know.

EMMA. Yes, but we must not rest our claims on that distinction. Many other counties, I believe, are also called the garden of England.

MRS. ELTON (*crosses to sit on sofa*). My brother and sister have promised us a visit in the summer and that will be our time for exploring. They will have their barouche-landau, of course, which holds four perfectly, without saying anything of *our* carriage. They could hardly come in their chaise at that season of the year. Do you have many exploring parties in the summer, Miss Woodhouse?

EMMA. I am afraid we are rather out of distance

from the popular beauty spots which attract the sort of parties you speak of.

MRS. ELTON. My caro sposo (*indicates her husband*) has assured me you have quite a musical society in Highbury, have you not, Mr. E.?

MR. ELTON. Yes indeed, my love, the ladies of Highbury are extremely talented.

MRS. ELTON. I hear on every side that Jane Fairfax is by far the most accomplished performer. I long to hear her. Jane Fairfax is absolutely charming. A sweet, interesting creature. So mild and ladylike, and her situation is so calculated to affect one's sympathy. Miss Woodhouse, we must exert ourselves and endeavour to do something for the poor unfortunate girl. She is so timid and silent, I am sure she suffers from being too sensitive.

EMMA. Then, madam, let us respect what little pride she has left and save her from further suffering.

MRS. ELTON. I can see you are not so experienced in charitable works as myself. I was never done giving advice to the poor in the neighbourhood of Maple Grove. I am determined to write to all my friends near Bath and Bristol imploring them to watch out for the right situation for dear Jane. Rest assured I shall find something at once, so many friends as I have.

MRS. ELTON. And now, Mr. E., our next call is at Randalls, is it not?

EMMA *crosses to bell-pull.*

MR. ELTON. Exactly so, Augusta, my love.

MRS. ELTON. I am told they are exceptionally charming people, both Mr. and Mrs. Weston, and Mr. Frank Churchill. So odd to drop one's father's name and still remain friends with him.

EMMA. Mr. Weston and his son are more than friends, Mrs. Elton; they are a devoted father and son.

MRS. ELTON (*rises, crosses* C.). Of course you know the family particularly well. Mrs. Weston was your governess, I think?

EMMA (*coldly*). Mrs. Weston is my dearest friend, madam.

MRS. ELTON. I am told she is quite ladylike.

EMMA. Mrs. Weston's manners were always particularly good.

MRS. ELTON. That is fortunate indeed, for I cannot bear the sight of ill-breeding in a woman.

EMMA. Indeed we are at one, madam; there are few things I find more difficult to bear.

MRS. ELTON. I am so pleased we are agreed on so many points, Miss Woodhouse. How quiet your little friend is — scarcely a word.

EMMA. I like to surround myself with quiet, unaffected people, and I think perhaps we have monopolised the conversation, have we not? Even Mr. Elton has been silenced. (SERLE *comes in.*) Mrs. Elton's carriage, Serle.

MRS. ELTON. When next we meet I shall be more thoroughly acquainted with the neighbourhood, and there will be so much more to talk about. Come, Mr. E., we really must be on our way. Good-bye, Miss Woodhouse, Miss ——?

MR. ELTON. Smith.

MRS. ELTON. Oh, Smith. (*Bobs and sweeps out.*)

EMMA. Good-bye, madam. Sir. (*Curtseys.*)

HARRIET *curtseys,* ELTON *bows. They go out.*

HARRIET (*crosses to* EMMA, *when the door has closed*). Well, Miss Woodhouse, what do you think of her

— is she not very charming and beautiful?

EMMA (*crosses* R.C.). A remarkably elegant gown. Most unsuitable for visiting, of course, and too showy for my taste, but it suited her very well indeed.

HARRIET (*biting her lips*). I am not at all surprised that she should have fallen in love with him or he with her.

EMMA. No surprise at all. A pretty fortune, she came his way, and so very unlikely she would get a better offer. It is not every's man's fate to marry the woman who loves him best.

HARRIET (*surprised at herself*). How remarkably composed I felt after all! Perhaps my mind was too taken up with meeting Mr. Martin.

EMMA. When have you met Mr. Martin, Harriet?

HARRIET. I think you are not yourself to-day, Miss Woodhouse. I have told you already. I met him at the haberdasher's when I went in about my spotted muslin. Only think, Miss Woodhouse, the door opened and who should walk in but Miss Elizabeth and Mr. Robert Martin.

EMMA. So that is what you were excited about when you came in?

HARRIET. Oh yes, Miss Woodhouse, I felt I should have fainted. He said how pleased he was to see me again and shook hands, and Elizabeth did too, and I took courage and said, "I must go." What Mrs. Ford thought I do not know, for the spotted muslin went quite out of my head.

EMMA (*with feeling*). Mr. Robert Martin seems to have some surprisingly gentle qualities for one so lowly placed.

HARRIET. Yes, he does, does he not, Miss Woodhouse?

EMMA. It must have been very distressing for you both, but you seem to have behaved extremely well and in so ladylike a manner. I am indeed proud of you, dearest Harriet.

HARRIET (*pleased*). You think I behaved in a ladylike manner? You really do, Miss Woodhouse? Mrs. Elton is very ladylike too, is she not? (*A break in her voice.*)

EMMA. Insufferable, absolutely insufferable, with her caro sposos, her Maple Groves and her barouche-landau. Oh, how I detest her.

HARRIET (*sniffing back her tears*). Oh, Miss Woodhouse, if you are saying this on my account you need not. With your help I shall get over Mr. Elton in time. (*Gulps back her tears.*) I wish them both the greatest of happiness, I'm sure. (*Bursts into tears and runs from the room.*)

EMMA (*calling after her*). Harriet, do not cry, I beg of you, do not cry. (*Harriet has disappeared.*) Poor Harriet, what can I say to comfort her? I who am so palpably to blame. I would willingly give her Mr. Churchill if he were not so obviously attracted to myself. . . . How I catch myself out. Frank Churchill comes regularly to my mind though I doubt if I am in love with him. . . . I like him exceedingly, but I think I should not like to marry him . . . or should I ? It would surely kill dear Papa. I wonder if Mr. Churchill will propose at the ball? . . . I think he is very much in love, but dare not declare himself because of his selfish aunt. (EMMA *goes to the long mirror* D.R., *where she studies herself.*) How should I best receive his proposal? (*She poses daintily, one hand held out gracefully.*) Or like this? (*Changes her position.*) You may hold my hand, sir, but I do not know what I shall answer. (*Laughs at herself — she lies back on the settee. Dreamily*) Emma Churchill of Enscombe. Oh — how pleasant a thing life is with a ball to look forward to.

She lies back on the settee and closes her eyes as her mind turns on the ball. The lights fade slowly and the Curtain as slowly descends.

[*Ballroom music to be played between this and the following scene.*]

SCENE II: *Early Summer — the Evening of the Ball*

[*N.B.—There need be no change of dress for* EMMA *for the opening of this scene.*]

The drawing-room has a festive look about it, due mostly to the profusion of flowers and the table set with a white cloth and glasses and the all-important punch-bowl, L. *of double doors.*

SERLE *is discovered at the fireplace where he has just placed a log on the fire. He peels off his white gloves, puts them in his tail pocket. From his inside breast pocket he takes a fresh pair of white gloves and puts them on carefully. He goes to the punch table and helps himself to a glass which he sips greedily, then remembering his manners he drinks it very genteelly, finger very much poised in the air. He is enjoying himself in this situation when* EMMA *comes in.*

EMMA. I trust the punch is to your taste, Serle.

SERLE *gulps and splutters.* EMMA *tries to look severe.* SERLE *immediately regains his poise.*

SERLE. A trifle on the sweet side, I thought, madam.

EMMA. I have not your experienced palate, Serle, but the punch is exactly to my liking.

SERLE. I am delighted to hear it, ma'am. (*Bows.*)

EMMA (*crosses* L.C.). Have you seen Miss Smith? I understood she was in her room dressing for the ball.

SERLE. The young lady left her dancing slippers at Mrs. Goddard's, ma'am. She said she would not bother the servants and insisted on fetching them herself.

EMMA. Thank you, Serle. Everything seems in order. Make sure the dining-room fire is kept going.

MR. WOODHOUSE *comes in wearing evening clothes.*

SERLE. Certainly, ma'am. (*Goes out.*)

MR. WOODHOUSE. What, are you not dressed, Emma? Our guests will be here at any moment.

EMMA. They will not be here for ages yet, Papa. Mrs. Weston is coming early to give her opinion on everything; when she does, then I shall start to dress.

MR. WOODHOUSE. But Mr. Weston will come with her, and Mr. Churchill, of course; and then I think I did invite Miss Bates to give her opinion and Miss Fairfax will come with her, so of course I had to ask Mr. Knightley.

EMMA. But, Papa, why did you not tell me? I shall not be ready to receive them.

MR. WOODHOUSE (*crosses to fire, rubbing hands*). Mrs. Weston is used to playing hostess for us. She will receive our old friends. The only stranger who is coming early will be Mrs. Elton, and she . . .

EMMA. Mrs. Elton! You asked Mrs. Elton to come early? Oh, Papa, how could you? I would rather die than have her find me unprepared. Why did you not tell me sooner?

MR. WOODHOUSE. Just one of my little surprises, my dear. You know how I like my little surprises.

EMMA. Yes, Papa.

MR. WOODHOUSE. Perhaps James has not yet gone to fetch Miss Bates and Miss Fairfax.

At this moment the french window rattles and a knock can be heard.

EMMA. Who can this be? (*She crosses to the window.*)

MR. WOODHOUSE (*frightened*). Careful, my love, careful. Decent people use the front door. That is the proper way to enter a house, by the front door.

The window rattles again and EMMA *peers out.*

EMMA. Mr. Churchill and Harriet! There has been some accident.

MR. WOODHOUSE. An accident! What an upheaval on the night of the ball.

EMMA *opens the window hurriedly.* FRANK *comes in wearing a cloak and riding boots. He is carrying* HARRIET, *who has fainted.*

EMMA (*worried*). Pray, sir, what has happened?

MR. WOODHOUSE. Is it an accident, sir?

FRANK. There is no need to worry. Miss Smith has merely been frightened.

He lays her on the couch. EMMA *fetches smelling salts from desk.*

EMMA. But how did it happen, pray? (*She holds the salts to* HARRIET'S *nose.*)

FRANK. Some gipsies accosted her on the lonely part of the Richmond Road near the wood. Your poor little friend took fright and tried to run up the bank. She fell, and they were about to pounce on her. Luckily I arrived on the scene and managed to beat them off.

MR. WOODHOUSE (*shaking*). Gipsies attacking our guests! What a dreadful thing. Secure the door as well, sir. We must inform the constabulary without delay.

FRANK. I doubt if that will be necessary, sir. They made off at some speed when I arrived.

MR. WOODHOUSE *sits on small sofa* — L. *of big sofa.* HARRIET *whimpers as she responds to* EMMA'S *treatment.*

EMMA. How very fortunate you happened to be there, sir. But why were you not at Randalls preparing for the ball?

FRANK. I am prepared, I changed at my aunt's house. I went to London to have my hair cut.

EMMA. And curled too, I see.

FRANK. Yes, curled too; do you not like it?

EMMA. Very pretty indeed.

FRANK. I did not go only to have my hair attended to. My aunt is seriously ill. She has had another attack. I must return to London first thing in the morning.

EMMA. But you shall return to Highbury again, sir?

FRANK. Indeed I shall, though I doubt when. My aunt is worse than I have seen her. It was with the greatest difficulty I could get away this evening.

EMMA. I am extremely sorry, sir. I trust Mrs. Churchill will soon be recovered.

HARRIET *whimpers.*

EMMA. I think she is coming round.

MR. WOODHOUSE. Nothing but trouble and violence. (*He has now seated himself.*) Poor Miss Smith. How is she, my dear?

EMMA. She will soon be out of it, Papa.

FRANK. I am sure she is not hurt. Your beautiful little friend, how frightened she must have been.

EMMA. And how grateful she must be to you, sir.

FRANK. Miss Smith told me she was on her way to fetch her dancing slippers from Mrs. Goddard's. I will fetch them for her now.

EMMA. Sir Galahad seems destined to be your role, Mr. Churchill. You are for ever rescuing fair ladies in the most romantic circumstances.

FRANK. Yes, I am indeed fortunate. And now if you will excuse me, Miss Woodhouse, I shall return in the shortest possible time. (*He bows.*)

MR. WOODHOUSE (*rises*). A very gallant rescue, sir. Do not leave us long unattended, I beg of you. One never knows with gipsies.

FRANK. I shall make all possible haste, sir.

EMMA *bobs. He goes out.*

MR. WOODHOUSE. Emma, my love, you must promise never to go alone on the Richmond Road again. I am all of a tremble. (*At door*) I must get Serle to give me half a glass of Madeira wine in water. Only half a glass.

He goes out.

EMMA. Yes, Papa. (HARRIET *begins to come to. She looks wildly round the room.*) You are safe now, dearest Harriet.

HARRIET (*clinging to her*). Oh, Miss Woodhouse, only think, they chased me. The gipsies chased me.

EMMA. There is no need to worry. The gipsies themselves have been chased by your noble rescuer.

HARRIET. How brave he was, Miss Woodhouse, and so kind and attentive to myself when I swooned.

EMMA. Do you feel able to sit up?

HARRIET *sits up. She is now beginning to enjoy the thought of her adventures.*

HARRIET. Only think, Miss Woodhouse, if he had not come along anything might have happened to me, anything! They might have — only think, Miss Woodhouse . . .

EMMA. I would rather not think, Harriet dear, and now if we do not get dressed quickly we shall be late for the ball.

HARRIET (*her eyes shining*). Mr. Churchill is a very good sort of man, is he not, Miss Woodhouse?

EMMA. He is indeed. Now run along and dress. Make yourself look your prettiest. I will be up directly Mrs. Weston arrives.

HARRIET. You are so kind to me, dear Miss Woodhouse.

EMMA. Remember you are the heroine of the hour.

HARRIET (*delighted*). Oh, am I, Miss Woodhouse, am I indeed?

She giggles and runs out.

EMMA. Yes, little Cinderella, and my Prince Charming has gone to fetch your slippers. . . . Can it be that poor Harriet has a love interest in Mr. Churchill? Certainly no circumstances could be more romantic. What was it Mr. Churchill said, " Your beautiful little friend, she must have been so very frightened." Can it be that Mr. Churchill returns Harriet's admiration? Surely not. . . . Can it be that he pays attention to every pretty girl he meets? . . . I should not be in the least surprised. . . . I think I have already cooled a little towards that gentleman. . . . When did I begin to cool — the moment I saw Harriet in his arms? . . . No, I think it was the moment he said he had been to London to have his hair attended. Imagine Mr. Knightley doing such a thing? (*Laughs at the thought.*) Still, it would be amusing if Mr. Churchill were to propose. . . . Indeed I shall be outraged if he does not, though what I should answer I am still in doubt. (*She crosses to fire.*)

MR. *and* MRS. WESTON *come in.*

MRS. WESTON (*going to* EMMA *and taking her in her arms*). My dearest Emma, what an upset this must have been.

MR. WESTON (C.). Frank stopped the carriage and broke the news to us. How is dear little Miss Smith?

EMMA. She is quite recovered.

MRS. WESTON. And you have not been able to dress yet, my dear.

EMMA. Papa has invited all our close friends to come and give their advice on everything before the other guests arrive. One of Papa's little surprises. Dear Mrs. Weston, I beg you to help me. If they should come before I am ready, will you be so good as to play hostess for me?

MRS. WESTON. Of course, my love.

MR. WESTON. And I will guard the portals against the vagrants and the gipsies.

EMMA (*at door*). How proud you must be of your son, Mr. Weston. So gallant a young man for any father to be proud of.

MR. *and* MRS. WESTON *beam happily at this praise.* EMMA *goes out.*

MR. WESTON (*crossing to* MRS. WESTON — *delighted*). There, what did I not tell you, Mrs. Weston? She has fallen in love with him.

MRS. WESTON. I think that she likes him, but when Emma is in love I am sure there will be no hiding it.

MR. WESTON (*sits desk chair*). We can have no doubt that Frank is in love, all this mooning about . . . listening to only half a conversation . . . dreamy-eyed and preoccupied as he is.

MRS. WESTON. How happy I should be if they were to make a match of it.

MR. WESTON. Wait and see, something will be decided before this evening is over, mark my words.

SERLE *comes in.*

SERLE. Mr. Knightley.

MR. KNIGHTLEY *comes in looking very handsome and distinguished in his evening suit.* SERLE *goes out.*

MRS. WESTON (*going forward*). Good evening, sir.

MR. KNIGHTLEY (*bows*). Good evening, madam — sir. Where is Emma? How is Emma?

MRS. WESTON. She will be here directly. There was a little upset, you know; it delayed her being ready.

MR. KNIGHTLEY. It is all over the town, and such a variety of stories have I heard, that I do not know what to believe.

MR. WESTON. It is nothing serious. Miss Smith was accosted by some gipsies, Frank came to her aid and that is all.

MR. KNIGHTLEY. This is indeed a relief. Rumour says Miss Smith has been carried away, Mr.

Churchill stabbed and Hartfield burnt to the ground.

MR. WESTON. So much for rumour.

MRS. WESTON. You have not heard it said that Miss Woodhouse is to marry her friend's gallant rescuer, have you, Mr. Knightley? For I should not be in the least surprised if that were to be the case.

MR. KNIGHTLEY. Come, Mrs. Weston, you are too sensible a lady to set out as a match-maker. Let us leave such childish games to Emma, who has not yet outgrown them.

MRS. WESTON (*good-humouredly*). We shall see, Mr. Knightley, we shall see.

MR. WESTON. Women know more about such things than we do, sir.

A disturbance is heard out in the hall.

MRS. WESTON. Listen, Miss Bates has arrived.

MR. KNIGHTLEY. Arrived for the ball so early?

MR. WESTON. Poor Miss Bates, we must expect her to be in a highly nervous condition.

SERLE *enters.*

SERLE. Miss Bates. Miss Fairfax.

MISS BATES (*as soon as she is within the room — to* SERLE). So very obliging of you. (SERLE *bows and goes out.*) Well, this is brilliant indeed. Nothing wanting, the hall so well lighted up. You must have Aladdin's lamp, Miss Woodhouse. . . . Oh, Miss Woodhouse is not here! Such a pretty room for dancing as the inner hall makes. Indeed Hartfield is the very first house in the neighbourhood. Miss Woodhouse is the first lady and Mr. Woodhouse the first gentleman. The very first in everything. (*Apologetically to the others*) Present company always excepted. I do not need to tell you that. A great pity Miss Woodhouse is not here. Such nice things as we are saying about her. (*She sits sofa.*)

MRS. WESTON (*crosses to sit small sofa*). Emma will be here directly. I have taken her place for the moment.

MISS BATES. Quite like old times, is it not, Mrs. Weston?

MRS. WESTON. How are you, Miss Bates, and you, Miss Fairfax?

MISS BATES. Very well, I thank you, ma'am. I hope you are quite well. No headache? . . . Delighted to hear it. Jane had a slight touch of cold . . . one of Jane's colds, you know.

MISS BATES (*noise of door opening*). Who is this? (MR. WOODHOUSE *comes in. During* MISS BATES' *speech*, MR. WESTON *talks quietly to* MISS FAIRFAX — *below punch table.*) Oh, dear Mr. Woodhouse, how do you do?

MR. WOODHOUSE. How are you, dear Miss Bates?

MISS BATES. Very well, thank you. This is a meeting quite in Fairyland. The hall is so prettily lit. We are so much obliged for the invitation, are we not, Jane?

JANE. Yes, indeed, sir.

MR. WOODHOUSE. The musicians have come so we will soon be able to start. If any of our guests arrive safe, I mean.

MR. KNIGHTLEY (*interrupting*). Come and sit down, sir. There is a long evening before you.

MR. WOODHOUSE. Thank you, Mr. Knightley. (*He sits armchair* U.L. — KNIGHTLEY *on his* L.) Such a dreadful business as this is. Poor Miss Smith, and poor dear Emma was so distressed over her little friend. I do trust she will not dance and tire herself out. If the gentlemen will have mercy and refrain from asking her, she will be quite safe.

MR. KNIGHTLEY. You need not look at me, sir, for I detest dancing and will invite no lady to tire herself out on my account.

MISS BATES. Ah, but you will not get Mr. Churchill to make such a promise, sir. Jane tells me he is a most accomplished dancer. Is he not, Jane, dear?

JANE. Yes, ma'am, Mr. Churchill is an excellent dancer.

MISS BATES. And do not be surprised if he should ask her for more than a partner in dancing. I have heard this very day he may ask her hand in marriage — only a whisper you know, but I should not be surprised.

JANE *looks away.*

MR. WOODHOUSE (*agitated*). Do not say such a thing, Miss Bates, it will not come to pass. I have had it from Emma herself that she will never marry. She would not do such a thing and break her poor father's heart. Mr. Churchill may be a very nice sort of young gentleman, but not for Emma, if you please.

MRS. WESTON. Would you like some refreshment, Miss Bates? Some coffee?

MISS BATES. Do I not hear another carriage? Who can this be? Upon my word this is charming, to be among such friends. Did you say coffee, Mrs. Weston? No coffee, I thank you. Never take coffee. A little tea by and by, no hurry. (*Her eye on the door.*)

MR. KNIGHTLEY. Come, Miss Bates, let us find the tea.

MISS BATES. Oh, Mr. Knightley, so very kind and

obliging indeed . . . so many kind friends. Miss Woodhouse sent the carriage — Jane and I quite ready — did not keep the horses a moment. Most comfortable carriage——

MR. KNIGHTLEY (*offering his arm*). Miss Bates . . .

MISS BATES. Oh, excuse me — your arm — so comforting as a gentleman's arm always is. (MISS BATES *and* MR. KNIGHTLEY *go out.*)

MR. WOODHOUSE. Allow me to show you the dining-room, Miss Fairfax.

JANE. Mr. Weston has promised to get me some punch, sir. I would rather stay here.

MR. WOODHOUSE. Then only half a glass at a time, that's my remedy. (*Goes out.*)

MR. WESTON. Now, Miss Fairfax, your punch. Shall you take a glass, my love?

MRS. WESTON. If you please, sir.

MR. WESTON *helps them to punch and they are about to drink when* SERLE *comes in.*

SERLE. Mr. and Mrs. Elton have arrived, madam.

MRS. WESTON. Bring them here, Serle, please (*crossing to fire*).

SERLE *is about to go out; as he turns round* MR. *and* MRS. ELTON *are in the doorway.* MRS. ELTON *is rather overdressed for a country ball. She makes a showy entrance, and immediately takes the floor.*

MRS. WESTON. Welcome to Hartfield.

MRS. ELTON. I trust we are not too early. Our carriage runs so smooth and our coachman is so quick I believe we drive faster than anybody. I see Miss Woodhouse is not here. Not here to welcome her guests. How very remiss. I hope we are not too early?

MRS. WESTON. Miss Woodhouse will be here directly.

MRS. ELTON. Jane, dear, how well you look, so very well turned out. Such taste.

JANE. You are too kind, madam.

MRS. ELTON (*crosses to fire*). You shall see how kind I am in a moment. I have great good news for you. How do you like my gown? You do not think there is too much trimming? I hope Wright has done my hair nicely?

JANE. Wright seems to have taken every care.

MRS. ELTON. Wright is the best maid in the world. Half French, of course. Such a pity it was her father who was English. A French name sounds so good in a maid, do you not think? I care little about dress for myself, but as a bride I feel it is expected of me. Do you like my pearls, Jane, my wedding present from Mr. Suckling?

SERLE *comes in.*

SERLE. Mr. Frank Churchill.

MRS. ELTON (*to* MR. WESTON). I am all impatience to meet your son, Mr. Weston. So much have I heard about him. I am known as a shrewd judge of character. I promise you my candid opinion of the young gentleman.

MRS. WESTON. We are well content with our own opinion of our son, Mrs. Elton.

FRANK *comes in. He is wearing becoming evening clothes.*

FRANK. Good evening, ladies. (*Bows.*) Gentlemen.

They all bid him good evening.

MRS. ELTON (*for all to hear*). A fine young man certainly is your son, sir. Present him to me at once.

MR. WESTON (*crosses to* FRANK, *then crosses to punch table*). Frank, come and meet Mrs. Elton.

FRANK (*bows*). Delighted, madam.

MRS. ELTON. I have just been telling your father how shrewd a judge of character I am, sir, and I promised him a candid opinion on yours.

FRANK. Pray do not disillusion my father, madam.

MRS. ELTON. On the contrary. My first impression, Mr. Weston, is one of complete approval.

FRANK. Thank you, madam.

MRS. WESTON. Give our friends some punch, my love.

MRS. ELTON. Our hostess is not yet dressed, it seems. Such behaviour is not known at Maple Grove. I confess I do not know how to take it.

MR. WESTON. Your punch, Mrs. Elton.

MRS. ELTON *crosses to sit sofa.* JANE *follows and sits* L. *of her.*

MRS. ELTON. Thank you. Jane, dearest, I cannot keep my news any longer, so excited am I. I have heard from my friend Mrs. Smallridge, and she is willing to have you as governess to her four children, merely on my recommendation. Mrs. Smallridge moves in the first circles, a charming lady, and she visits at Maple Grove.

JANE. You are too kind, madam. I do not intend to leave Highbury for some time yet. I am most grateful for Mrs. Smallridge's offer, but I beg leave to think the matter over.

MRS. ELTON. You could never find a situation more to your liking. Mrs. Smallridge is quite the lady, I assure you. You will be better paid at Mrs. Smallridge's than anywhere. You will not find such kindness anywhere in England.

EMMA *comes in followed by* HARRIET. *Both look charming.* FRANK *goes forward to meet them.*

FRANK. Dearest ladies, your presence brightens the room like summer sunshine; standing there as you do together makes indeed a picture to remember. (*He kisses both their hands.*)

EMMA. You are too gallant, sir.

MRS. ELTON (*she crosses to* ELTON *at fireplace*). The very words Mr. Elton used when he met me in the Assembly rooms at Bath.

EMMA. Pray forgive me, Mrs. Elton, an unavoidable delay. I was told the musicians were here. Come and take some refreshment before the other guests arrive.

MRS. ELTON. We are very fortunate at Maple Grove; the ballroom has a dining-room leading straight from it.

EMMA. I trust you will not feel too homesick, Mrs. Elton; although our ballroom is but an improvised one, the dining-room also leads off it.

MRS. WESTON *puts her arm round* EMMA *and they go out.* MR. WESTON *follows with* HARRIET.

MRS. ELTON (*snappily*). Come, Mr. E., give me your arm.

MR. ELTON. Yes, Augusta, my love.

They follow EMMA *and the* WESTONS *out.* JANE *has risen to go.* FRANK *detains her.*

FRANK. What is this nonsense about a situation? What does this mean?

JANE. It is none of my doing, sir. Mrs. Elton has taken the matter completely out of my hands.

FRANK. I will not have it. How dare Mrs. Elton!

JANE. Nevertheless, sir, I am determined to accept the situation.

FRANK. I will not tolerate it. The future Mrs. Churchill of Enscombe out as a governess. It will not do, Jane.

JANE. I fear there is so much more chance of my being a governess than of ever being Mrs. Churchill, that it would be better for all concerned if I were to quit Highbury for good. There is nothing for me to live for here. (*Crosses and sits stool* D.L.)

FRANK (*following* JANE). Do I count as nothing?

JANE. You have gone too far in your deception, sir. Everyone is waiting for you to propose to Miss Woodhouse. The rumour is on every tongue. I cannot bear to witness your attention to another any longer. I must go before my heart will break. (*Crosses* D.R. FRANK *follows.*)

FRANK. Jane, you must be sensible. It is known I cannot marry anyone while my aunt is in her present state of health. She would cut me off without hesitation. I am entirely dependent on Mrs. Churchill and she knows it.

JANE. It will not do. The strain of so much secrecy is too great for me. Our meetings are worse to bear than our separations. Have no fear, sir, you will soon forget me. Miss Woodhouse is a very charming lady, so obviously the right wife for you. Even Mrs. Churchill could not disapprove of such a daughter-in-law. Emma Woodhouse has fortune, the right connections, everything. . . .

FRANK. Mrs. Churchill would disapprove of any daughter-in-law. (*Pause.*) Jane, it occurs to me that I have been exceedingly selfish. I have no right to hold you down to so hopeless a prospect as myself.

JANE. Then you wish that we should both have our freedom, sir?

FRANK. No, I do not wish anything of the kind, Jane. Do you love me enough to marry me in spite of Mrs. Churchill — to risk her disapproval — to share poverty with me?

JANE. I love you too much, sir, to allow you to make such a sacrifice. You do not know the humiliation of poverty. You who have always had so much of everything. You would not love me long in poverty, sir.

FRANK. I cannot live without you, Jane.

JANE (*crosses* C.). You must, sir. I am determined. If I leave you now, I go knowing we love each other. The knowledge of your love will give me comfort for the rest of my life.

FRANK (*determined*). I will not give you up, Jane. I will go to my aunt in the morning and tell her everything.

JANE. No, sir, you must not, I beg of you.

MISS BATES *comes in.* FRANK *goes out.*

MISS BATES. Jane, dearest, there you are. The dear Coles have arrived and are inquiring for you. Pray come at once.

JANE. Yes, Aunt, at once.

MISS BATES. So nice Mrs. Coles was, and Mr. Coles. So nice as the dear Coles always are——

MRS. ELTON *comes in.*

MRS. ELTON (*crosses to sit sofa*). Jane, dear, you look quite flushed. I know how excited you must feel. So lovely is Mrs. Smallridge's estate. Nearly the size of Maple Grove.

JANE. You shall have my decision before the evening is out, I promise, Mrs. Elton.

MRS. ELTON. When you have seen as much of the world as I have, dear Jane, you will realise how many candidates there always are for the first situations. What more could a young lady desire than to be in Mrs. Smallridge's employ. Only think! Wax candles in the schoolroom. You may imagine how desirable! (*Music begins to play off-stage.*)

MISS BATES. Think well before you decide, Jane, dear, think well. (*She goes to the door.*) We can manage a little longer, and our neighbours are so kind, so very kind. What would my dear Papa have said. His granddaughter out alone in the world. Oh, it seems the ball has commenced.

She goes out.

MRS. ELTON (*rises, crosses* L.C.). Let us not hide ourselves away like this. The gentlemen will not know where to find us.

JANE (*crosses* D.R. *and sits armchair*). I scarcely feel in the mood for dancing.

FRANK *comes in with* EMMA *on one arm and* HARRIET *on the other — to* D.L. MR. KNIGHTLEY (D.R.), MR. (D.R.) *and* MRS. WESTON (C.) *follow, with* MR. ELTON (R.C.) *in the rear.*

HARRIET. One thing very dull, sir?

FRANK. No, one thing very *clever*, two things moderately clever, or three things——

FRANK and EMMA. — very dull indeed! (*Laugh.*)

MR. WESTON. The ball is about to be opened, ladies. Gentlemen, choose your partners.

FRANK. I have chosen mine, sir. Miss Woodhouse has done me the honour.

EMMA. The honour is mine, sir.

MR. WESTON. And you will be the handsomest

couple in the ballroom, I am convinced.

MRS. ELTON. What, no offer for the bride? Must I dance with my own caro sposo?

MR. WESTON. Indeed no, madam, if you will do me the honour?

MRS. ELTON. The honour, sir, is yours. Mr. E., you must dance with Mrs. Weston, then we shall be quits.

MR. ELTON. Most readily, Mrs. Weston, if you will dance with me?

MRS. WESTON. Me! No, no, I would get you a better partner than myself. I am no dancer.

MR. ELTON. Then if Miss Fairfax wishes to dance I shall have great pleasure, I am sure.

JANE. I have just told Mrs. Elton I am in no dancing mood, sir.

MRS. ELTON. Jane said so just before you came in, Mr. E.

MRS. WESTON. Here is another young lady disengaged whom I should be very glad to see dancing — Miss Smith.

MR. ELTON. Miss Smith — oh! — I had not observed. You are extremely obliging, Mrs. Weston. If I were not an old married man I should be delighted, but I fear my dancing days are over.

MRS. ELTON *is delighted at this reply and smiles encouragingly. There is an extremely uncomfortable atmosphere in the room. No one speaks for a moment until* MR. KNIGHTLEY *saves the situation.*

MR. KNIGHTLEY (*goes to Harriet*). It is as well, sir, for you should have been refused. Miss Smith has already promised this dance to me. (*Crosses* D.L. *with* HARRIET.)

The tension relaxes at once. EMMA *is all gratitude to* MR. KNIGHTLEY, *and there is a look of understanding between them.*

EMMA (*to* FRANK). We are pushed aside, sir. Mr. Knightley and Miss Smith must surely be the handsomest couple in the ballroom. Come, let us begin.

MISS BATES *comes running in excitedly.*

MISS BATES. Mr. Churchill — Mr. Churchill! Oh, dear Mr. Churchill, pray tell me once again how to play that amusing game. I have been trying to tell it to the dear Coles but I keep forgetting.

FRANK. It is very simple and merely demands that each player shall either say one thing very clever, two things moderately clever, or three things very dull indeed.

MISS BATES. Oh, that will not be difficult. I shall be sure to say three dull things as soon as I open my mouth.

EMMA (*unable to resist*). Ah, madam, but you will be limited as to the number — only three at once.

EMMA *laughs out loud at her own joke.* MISS BATES *does not realise she has been mocked and laughs. She turns to* MRS. ELTON, *who is glaring disapproval at* EMMA. MISS BATES *begins to realise; she is quite crestfallen.*

MISS BATES. Ah, to be sure, I see what you mean and I will try to hold my tongue. I fear I must make myself very disagreeable by talking too much. I am sure I do not mean to make myself disagreeable.

MRS. ELTON. Come, Miss Bates, I shall take you to the good Coles. I trust they will play the game as it should be played, in a spirit of goodwill.

MISS BATES. You are indeed kind, Mrs. Elton. Everyone is so kind.

MRS. ELTON. Come, Mr. Weston, if you please, you are to partner me, are you not? (*Holds her arm out invitingly.*)

MR. ELTON. Come, Mrs. Weston, let us see what the card players are doing.

They follow the others out. MR. KNIGHTLEY *moves to* EMMA. *Addresses her quietly but emphatically.*

MR. KNIGHTLEY. Emma! I have often known you to be thoughtless and foolish, but never deliberately cruel.

EMMA. Have you no sense of humour, sir? 'Twas merely a jest.

MR. KNIGHTLEY. If that is your idea of humour, I am glad I have none. Your arm, Miss Smith. (*Holds out his arm.*)

HARRIET (*gazing at him*). Yes, sir. (*Bobs.*)

They go out.

JANE (*after a moment*). Miss Woodhouse, with your kind permission, could James drive me home now? I am far from being in the mood for gaiety.

EMMA. Certainly, Miss Fairfax, if you really must leave us so soon.

JANE. Do not think me ungrateful, I beg of you. To-night I have made a decision. This must be my farewell to my friends in Highbury. I find it is more than I can bear. I shall write to Mrs. Elton's friend that I wish to commence the situation without delay. (*She is overcome with emotion.*) Miss Woodhouse, will you be so good as to tell my aunt I have a headache and have gone home. I could not bear to give an explanation now.

EMMA. I shall indeed, Miss Fairfax. I understand your feeling, but I wish that you could stay and enjoy the ball.

JANE. You are too kind, Miss Woodhouse, but please bear with me and understand. I could not endure it, truly I could not. Good night, and thank you again.

EMMA. Good night, Miss Fairfax.

FRANK (*with suppressed emotion*). Permit me to show you to your carriage, Miss Fairfax.

JANE (*quietly emphatic*). No, sir, I beg of you, allow me to go alone.

She bobs and goes out.

EMMA. Poor Miss Fairfax is quite upset. Never have I known her show so much warmth of feeling.

FRANK. Please, I would rather talk about you, Miss Woodhouse. Now that we are alone I cannot hold off any longer.

EMMA (*taking up the position she has rehearsed, feigning surprise*). Yes, sir, there is something you wish to say?

FRANK (*sits* L. *of* EMMA *on sofa*). From the very first moment I saw you, Miss Woodhouse, I felt there was a bond of sympathy between us.

EMMA. Yes, sir. I felt it too.

FRANK. Miss Woodhouse, I do not know how to begin. It is something which has been on my mind ever since my first visit to Hartfield, something which concerns you, myself, and one other.

EMMA. What can it be, sir, that you find so difficult to say?

FRANK. Pray forgive me, Miss Woodhouse. My lips are sealed. I cannot say what it is only fair to you I should say.

EMMA. Fair to me, sir? I do not understand.

FRANK. If I tell you it concerns my future wife. The loveliest creature God has ever created.

EMMA (*looking away*). You are too gallant, sir.

FRANK. If I tell you I cannot be open as other men can be, if I had not given my promise to a certain lady.

EMMA (*thinking he means his aunt*). I am not without understanding, sir. I have a similar situation with dear Papa. He is determined I shall never marry.

FRANK (*rises, crosses* C.). Why are old people so abominably selfish?

EMMA. It is not selfishness with Papa, it is merely that he loves me so very much he cannot bear to lose me.

FRANK. How well I know what he means. To lose the thing you love most. To be unable to claim what is rightfully yours. I cannot bear it. (*Looks at* EMMA *intently*). Dear Miss Woodhouse, I cannot bear England any longer. I have decided to go abroad.

EMMA (*rises*). Decided to go abroad! What does this mean, sir?

FRANK. England has no charm for me now. In spite of my aunt's protestations I shall leave for Swisserland without delay.

FRANK *is now feverishly walking up and down the room* — L.C.

EMMA. Pray calm yourself, sir. You seem almost as distressed as poor Miss Fairfax.

FRANK. I cannot bear to think of it. Never have I witnessed such suffering, such distress.

EMMA. Nor had I until I witnessed yours, sir.

FRANK (*impulsively*). Miss Woodhouse, if you will

forgive me, I shall accompany Miss Fairfax to her aunt's house.

EMMA. You mean to go now, sir?

FRANK. Considering the lady's present state of mind, it is a duty I cannot neglect.

EMMA (*crossing to* D.L.). I would not for the world have you neglect your duty on my account, sir. (*She is both bewildered and peeved.*)

FRANK. I will return at the earliest possible moment. (*Takes* EMMA'S *hand tenderly and kisses it.*) I am all gratitude, dear lady.

He bows and hurries out.

EMMA (*looks after him*). Indeed, never have I known such behaviour. To look at one as he did and say " I cannot bear England any longer, I shall go to Swisserland without delay ". . . . This is not at all what I had expected. The proposal of marriage turns out to be a proposal for sympathy and understanding. . . . Can it be that I, Miss Woodhouse of Hartfield, have been slighted? Surely he would not dare. (*Crosses to fire.*)

MRS. WESTON *comes in.*

MRS. WESTON. Emma, my love, we cannot begin the ball without you. I have tried to engage the guests in amusement, hoping you were delayed on an important matter. Frank was here with you, was he not?

EMMA. He was, madam.

MRS. WESTON. Have you not something to tell me? Some announcement to make?

EMMA. Simply that the ball must begin without me.

MRS. WESTON. What can you mean, Emma?

EMMA. Would you have me take the floor without

a partner, madam? (*Flounces across the room in a pet.*)

MRS. WESTON. Where is Frank? What has happened?

EMMA. The gentleman is going to Swisserland, madam, where I trust he will enjoy himself! (*Sits.*)

A gasp of amazement from MRS. WESTON. *Both ladies fan themselves briskly as*

The Curtain falls

ACT III

SCENE I: *Morning after the Ball*

EMMA *is discovered at the writing-desk. She seems to have difficulty in concentrating and all but nibbles the end of the quill. With an effort she pulls her straying thoughts together and writes vigorously.*

After a moment MR. KNIGHTLEY *appears at the french windows. He carries a bunch of particularly beautiful roses.*

MR. KNIGHTLEY. Good morning, Emma.

EMMA (*startled*). Good morning, sir.

MR. KNIGHTLEY. I trust I am not intruding.

EMMA. You know you are always welcome at Hartfield, sir.

A feeling of strain between them makes an awkward silence.

MR. KNIGHTLEY (*holds out the flowers*). I brought you these.

EMMA (*she rises*). Donwell roses; how very lovely, and such fragrance. You are all kindness, sir. I shall have them here beside me on the writing-desk. (*Rings bell.*)

Another awkward pause.

MR. KNIGHTLEY. I have interrupted your correspondence.

EMMA. I was writing a note to Isabella. I had finished but for my signature.

MR. KNIGHTLEY. To Isabella, eh? Then I shall

deliver it for you. I am going to visit our relations to-day.

EMMA (*surprised*). You are going to London, sir? Is this not a sudden scheme?

MR. KNIGHTLEY. It has been on my mind for some time.

SERLE *comes in.*

EMMA. Bring a tall vase with some water please, Serle.

SERLE. Yes, ma'am.

Goes out.

EMMA. Shall you be gone long, sir?

MR. KNIGHTLEY. A week or two at the most.

EMMA. But you will surely be back in time for my garden party. Never as long as I can remember have you missed a strawberry gathering at Hartfield.

MR. KNIGHTLEY. Then I shall endeavour to return in time. Have you anything to send to London besides the letter, or anything to say besides the love which nobody ever carries?

EMMA (*she crosses* D.R.). Thank you, no, sir. Papa has not left his room to-day. The excitement of last evening's entertainment was too much for him.

MR. KNIGHTLEY. I shall go to him presently.

SERLE *comes in with the vase.*

EMMA. Thank you, Serle. Would you put it here, please? (*Indicates piano.*)

MR. KNIGHTLEY. Let me arrange them while you finish your letter.

EMMA. Oh, thank you, sir.

SERLE *goes out.* EMMA *re-seats herself and signs the letter with a flourish.*

MR. KNIGHTLEY (*making conversation*). How is Miss

Smith to-day? I trust she is none the worse for her adventure?

EMMA. As I did not come down to breakfast I have not seen her yet. (*Looks at him and speaks to the point*) Mr. Knightley, I have written to Isabella asking her to invite Harriet to stay. I think it would do her good to forget the disappointments of Highbury for a while.

MR. KNIGHTLEY. An excellent idea.

EMMA (*she crosses to piano*). If she is at Brunswick Square while you are there, will you, for my sake, be kind to her?

MR. KNIGHTLEY. Surely it is not necessary to ask. Besides, I have grown to have something of a regard for Miss Smith. She is by no means the empty-headed girl I thought on meeting her at first. Furthermore, no one can deny she is exceedingly pretty, has a warm heart and tender feelings.

EMMA (*hands him the letter*). That from you, sir, is praise indeed. Would that some others had your understanding of her value. I have not known how to face her after last night's behaviour by a certain gentleman.

They are both arranging the flowers in the vase, MR. KNIGHTLEY *below piano,* EMMA L. *of it.*

MR. KNIGHTLEY. There again I thought she showed herself so superior to both Mr. and Mrs. Elton.

EMMA. In the instance of Mr. Elton, the praise was due to you entirely, sir. I cannot express the gratitude I felt for your gallant gesture at that moment.

MR. KNIGHTLEY *crosses to* L.C.

MR. KNIGHTLEY. Thank you, Emma. (*Pauses*

awkwardly before he speaks again.) And now I must once more speak to you as I have been used to: a privilege rather endured than allowed perhaps, but I still must use it.

EMMA. Where have I done mischief now, sir?

MR. KNIGHTLEY. I cannot see you acting wrong without a remonstrance. How could you be as unfeeling as you were to Miss Bates last evening? How could you be so insolent to a woman of her age and situation?

EMMA (*tries to laugh it off*). How could I help saying what I did? It was not so very bad. I dare say she did not understand.

MR. KNIGHTLEY. Believe me, she did; she talked of it afterwards, while defending you against Mrs. Elton. If you could have but heard her forbearance, indeed you would have been ashamed.

EMMA. Oh, I know there is not a better creature in the world, but you must allow that what is good and what is ridiculous are most unfortunately blended in her.

MR. KNIGHTLEY. But, Emma, to ridicule a harmless old woman, to laugh at her outright in the presence of others, is deplorable.

EMMA. But I did not mean it, sir. It seemed an amusing thing to say at the moment, and as I like saying amusing things, I said it.

MR. KNIGHTLEY. It seems to me, Emma, it is time you grew out of being a spoilt and selfish child into a sensible woman. All your life you have had your way in ruling your family. Now you would try to rule the lives of others. Think what harm you have done to Harriet Smith and Robert Martin alone.

EMMA (*crosses to desk, her lips quivering*). What I

did was done for their own good.

MR. KNIGHTLEY. In your opinion only. So conceited have you become that it does not occur to you that your opinion could be wrong. You do not think that the all-important Miss Woodhouse of Hartfield could have a wrong opinion. If you could give some of your spare time to managing your own conduct and leave others to manage theirs, the advantage would be felt by all concerned.

EMMA (*trying to check tears of annoyance*). If you have any further faults to find, Mr. Knightley, give them to me quickly before I leave you.

MR. KNIGHTLEY. There is nothing further I can think of other than that you are spoilt, selfish and meddlesome to a degree, and you may save yourself the trouble of quitting the room, for it is I who shall take my leave of you. (*Moves to the door.*)

HARRIET *comes in carrying a small parcel. They collide.*

HARRIET (*she crosses to* EMMA, L.C.). There you are, Miss Woodhouse, I have been looking for you all the morning. (*Looks at* MR. KNIGHTLEY, *bobs.*) Good morning, sir.

MR. KNIGHTLEY. Good morning, Miss Smith. It is indeed a pleasure to see you. I trust you are well?

HARRIET (*delighted by his interest*). Yes, indeed, sir, very well, thank you, sir. (*Giggles.*)

EMMA (*controls herself admirably, but she is very subdued*). Mr. Knightley has come to say good-bye, Harriet. He is on his way to London.

HARRIET (*disappointed*). You are going away, sir?

MR. KNIGHTLEY. Only for a short stay. I could not be separated from the attractions of Highbury for long.

HARRIET *looks to the ground.*

EMMA. Would you like to go to London, Harriet?

HARRIET. Oh, Miss Woodhouse, I should love it above all things. One sometimes gets a little tired of Highbury, do you not think?

EMMA. I understand, Harriet, and you shall go to London. Mr. Knightley is carrying a message to my sister in Brunswick Square. She will be delighted to accommodate you, I know.

HARRIET (*delighted*). Dear Miss Woodhouse, how can I ever thank you. (*To* MR. KNIGHTLEY) And you are to be there too, sir?

MR. KNIGHTLEY (*nods*). I shall take good care of you, Miss Smith. We must arrange a programme of enjoyment.

HARRIET. Oh, sir, what shall it be?

MR. KNIGHTLEY. Now let me think. Perhaps a picnic at St. James's, a visit to the Gardens at Kew, an evening at the play . . .

HARRIET (*ecstatically happy*). Oh, sir, a visit to the play!

MR. KNIGHTLEY. And perhaps — mind, I only say perhaps — I may persuade my brother and sister-in-law to give a ball in your honour at Brunswick Square.

HARRIET (*brimming over with excitement*). A ball in my honour! Oh, sir, you are too good. If only you could be there too, Miss Woodhouse.

EMMA. You must not give Isabella too much trouble, sir. Consider her health. Besides, her time is occupied enough with the children.

MR. KNIGHTLEY. That is a matter for Isabella to decide, is it not, Emma?

EMMA. Yes, sir, but . . .

MR. KNIGHTLEY. And now, with your permission, I shall pay my respects to Mr. Woodhouse.

EMMA (*humbly*). Thank you, sir.

MR. KNIGHTLEY. Ladies.

He smiles at both and goes out.

HARRIET. Mr. Knightley is the nicest sort of gentleman, is he not, Miss Woodhouse? I like him extremely.

EMMA (*she crosses to below sofa* R.). He has expressed his liking for you too, Harriet.

HARRIET. Oh, has he, Miss Woodhouse? Has he really? I do not know how to thank you for the visit to London, especially as Mr. Knightley is to be there.

EMMA. If only I could do more to assure your happiness, dearest Harriet.

HARRIET. Miss Woodhouse, I have a sort of confession to make.

EMMA (*she sits sofa*). A confession. Pray, Harriet, what is it?

HARRIET. Can you guess what this parcel holds? (*Undoes parcel.*)

EMMA. Not the least in the world. Did *he* ever give you anything?

HARRIET. No, I cannot call them gifts, though I have put a foolish value on them.

EMMA (*curious, in spite of herself*). Pray what is in the box, Harriet?

HARRIET (*she kneels* L. *of* EMMA). Only some pebbles he found while out walking. He showed them to me, and as I admired the pretty colours he asked me to have them for myself. (*She holds out the box for* EMMA *to see.*)

EMMA. Yes, they are very pretty indeed. But what is this?

HARRIET. A pencil stump. The part without any lead. *He* used it.

EMMA. Oh, Harriet, he meant so much to you that you kept these pitiful relics. You make me feel ashamed.

HARRIET (*she rises and crosses to* D.R.). You need not be, Miss Woodhouse. I must now get rid of these keepsakes, then I am done with him for ever.

EMMA. Bravely said, dearest. I know that one day, when you are comfortably married, you will laugh at these girlish feelings.

HARRIET (*quietly*). I shall never marry.

EMMA. Never marry! This is a new resolution, is it not?

HARRIET. However, it is one that I shall never change.

EMMA. I hope this is not in compliment to Mr. Elton.

HARRIET. Mr. Elton indeed! Oh, no. (*Reverently*) So superior to Mr. Elton.

EMMA (*in some alarm*). My dearest Harriet, I beg of you to use discretion before you form so hopeless an attachment.

HARRIET. Oh, Miss Woodhouse, I have not the presumption to suppose . . . indeed I am not so mad. But it gives me the greatest pleasure just to admire him from a distance, and to think how infinitely superior he is to all the rest of the men in the world. Even if he were married to another I should feel the same for him.

EMMA. I confess I am not surprised, Harriet. The service he rendered you alone was enough to warm a colder heart than yours.

HARRIET. How well you understand, Miss Woodhouse. When I saw him coming towards me . . . his noble look, and my wretchedness before, I changed in one moment from perfect misery to perfect happiness.

EMMA (*touched*). Dearest Harriet, you have a nature to be envied.

HARRIET. Miss Woodhouse, have I your permission to bury the box somewhere in the garden? I would like to have done with it.

EMMA. Of course, Harriet. Bury it wherever you wish.

SERLE *comes in.*

SERLE. Mr. and Mrs. Weston to see Miss Woodhouse.

EMMA. Show them in, Serle.

SERLE. Yes, ma'am.

He goes out.

HARRIET. Would you mind if I run out into the garden with this? (*She picks up the little box.*) I do not wish to give an explanation of it.

EMMA. You are very wise, Harriet. Come back when you have done.

HARRIET. It will not take me long. (*Goes to the window, looks at the box.*) I think, Miss Woodhouse, there is nothing so dead as dead love.

She goes out into the garden leaving EMMA *extremely perplexed.*

EMMA (*she crosses to* L.C., *looking after* HARRIET). Harriet behaves in the strangest manner. I trust this latest disappointment cannot have unhinged her mind.

SERLE *enters, followed by* MR. *and* MRS. WESTON.

SERLE. Mr. and Mrs. Weston.

MRS. WESTON. Emma, dearest, we have but a moment. The most distressing news.

EMMA. Pray be seated. Tell me what has happened.

MRS. WESTON *sits armchair* U.L., MR. WESTON L. *of her by fire.*

MR. WESTON. No sooner had we arrived at Randalls last night after the ball, when a message came urging Frank to make haste to Richmond. His aunt, Mrs. Churchill, was gravely ill.

MRS. WESTON. She had taken a stroke . . . most unexpected.

MR. WESTON. Frank made off with all possible speed.

MRS. WESTON. And now we have had a note from him. Mrs. Churchill died shortly after his arrival, without recognising him.

EMMA. I am indeed sorry to hear it.

MRS. WESTON. Emma, there is something else. The most unaccountable business. I do not know how to begin. (*To* MR. WESTON) Pray you tell her, sir.

MR. WESTON. No, no, my love, you will break it better than I can. With your permission, Miss Woodhouse, I shall stroll in the garden while she does it.

He goes out of french windows.

EMMA. In heaven's name what is it? Some accident . . . something has happened at Brunswick Square? Tell me at once, dear madam, I am all alarmed.

MRS. WESTON. It relates to Frank. His letter also announces an attachment. . . .

EMMA. An attachment. This is no surprise to me.

MRS. WESTON. Oh, but it is more than an attachment. A positive engagement.

EMMA. An engagement!

MRS. WESTON. What will you say, Emma, when I tell you that Frank Churchill and Miss Fairfax have been engaged since the autumn?

EMMA. Jane Fairfax! Good God! Oh, my poor Harriet. You are not serious? You do not mean it?

MRS. WESTON (*nods*). The engagement was formed at Weymouth and kept a secret from everybody.

EMMA. Well, this is a circumstance I must think of for half a day before I can comprehend it.

MRS. WESTON. Mr. Weston and I have no words to express our disappointment. We had such hopes that you and Frank — that Frank and you——

EMMA. Do not be miserable on my account, dear friend. My affections are in no way caught up with Mr. Churchill.

MRS. WESTON. Are you sincere, Emma?

EMMA. Truly, madam, I assure you.

MRS. WESTON. It does my heart good to hear you say it. On this point we have been quite wretched.

EMMA. Poor Miss Fairfax! Only now do I realise her dilemma. She must have considered me a rival. But in allowing her to apply for the post as governess Mr. Churchill was surely most indelicate——

MRS. WESTON. That was all Mrs. Elton's doing. Frank knew nothing of it until last evening at the ball. He told me on the way home how the news had shocked him.

EMMA. That is indeed a point in his favour.

MRS. WESTON. In the letter he sent, Frank requests that I should ask you to suspend judgement on him until he has the opportunity to beg your understanding in person.

EMMA (*thinking*). So that is what he meant. " My lips are sealed — a promise to a certain lady ". . . . I understood him to mean Mrs. Churchill. The fault is mine only. I was wrong, my imagination led me astray.

MRS. WESTON. And now we must pay our call on Miss Fairfax, to acquaint her with our knowledge. (*She goes to the window and beckons to* MR. WESTON.) My love!

EMMA. No doubt Mr. Churchill has already done so.

MR. WESTON *comes in at once.*

EMMA. You are fortunate in your daughter-in-law, sir.

MR. WESTON (*he crosses* C.). As his father, I must now give my blessing. Happily I have always had a high regard for Miss Fairfax.

EMMA. Miss Fairfax has excellent qualities. Pray give her my fondest greetings.

HARRIET *comes in.*

HARRIET. Good morning, ma'am. (*Bobs.*)

MRS. WESTON. Good morning, Miss Smith. I trust you are none the worse of last night's encounter?

HARRIET. I am quite recovered, thank you, Mrs. Weston.

MR. WESTON. Now, my dear, we must hasten to Miss Fairfax as Frank requested.

MRS. WESTON *crosses to* EMMA — *embrace.*

MRS. WESTON. How good you are, dear Emma. You have such understanding. So much more generous than the gentleman deserves.

MR. WESTON. We shall call again later in the day

when there is more time to spare.

EMMA. I am always happy to see you both. (MRS. WESTON *kisses* EMMA. *They both bow to* HARRIET *and go out.*) Well, Harriet, is your duty performed?

HARRIET. It is done, and I am glad it is done. Now I have finished with the gentleman.

EMMA. Harriet, did Mr. Weston tell you anything while you were both in the garden?

HARRIET. Nothing of importance. Merely that Mr. Churchill and Miss Fairfax are to be married; is that not the oddest thing, Miss Woodhouse?

EMMA (*surprised*). What do you mean, Harriet? Is this not the gentleman we were discussing before the Westons arrived?

HARRIET. I do not understand you, Miss Woodhouse.

EMMA. Harriet, do you mean to tell me Mr. Churchill's engagement was not a great shock to you?

HARRIET. Yes indeed, it came as a surprise. I have not your talent for seeing into everybody's heart, Miss Woodhouse.

EMMA. Upon my word, I begin to doubt if I have any such talent. I never had the slightest idea of his attachment to Miss Fairfax. You know that if I had I should most certainly have cautioned you.

HARRIET (*astonished*). Me! Why should you caution me? You do not think that I care about Mr. Frank Churchill?

EMMA. But you said you loved him as he came towards you with such a noble look and you were in such misery with the gipsies crowding round you.

HARRIET (*with feeling*). I did not mention the gipsies, Miss Woodhouse. Truly I did not. I meant his noble look as he saved me from disgrace when that horrid Mr. Elton slighted me over the opening dance.

EMMA (*desperately*). Harriet, let us understand each other without the possibility of further mistake. Are you speaking of . . . of Mr. Knightley?

HARRIET. Oh, Miss Woodhouse, you will not set yourself against it. You are too good to put difficulties in the way — say you will not!

EMMA. Have you any idea of Mr. Knightley returning your affection, Harriet?

HARRIET. Yes, I must say I have, but not fearfully. He has been most tender in his attentions. I can but hope he will propose. Perhaps he will do so when we are in London together. He may even do so when he takes me to Kew Gardens.

EMMA (*sharply*). Enough, Harriet.

HARRIET. Is something wrong, Miss Woodhouse?

EMMA. This news comes as rather a surprise to me, Harriet. I beg of you to leave me alone to think it out.

HARRIET. You are not angry with me, are you, Miss Woodhouse? I have not done wrong? Tell me I have not done wrong.

EMMA (*pats her shoulder*). Forgive me, Harriet, of course you have not done wrong. I did not mean to speak sharply. I do not even know why I did. I will come and find you later, but please leave me now.

HARRIET. Yes, Miss Woodhouse. (*At door*) Love is indeed an extraordinary kind of thing, is it not, Miss Woodhouse?

Without waiting for a reply she goes out somewhat sad and perplexed. EMMA *immediately begins to pace the room.*

EMMA. But Mr. Knightley! Why did she have to fall in love with Mr. Knightley? He is so much her superior in years . . . in everything. (*Pauses — speaks quietly.*) Why is it so much worse that Harriet should be in love with Mr. Knightley than with Mr. Churchill. . . . Oh no, good heavens! No, it cannot be . . . it hits me with the speed of an arrow. I am in love with Mr. Knightley myself! At last I find myself in love. . . . But what of Mr. Knightley? . . . I have always been first with him. . . . But what did Harriet say? He was tender to her, and good heavens! Did not Mr. Knightley himself say he had grown to have an opinion of Harriet? And now I have sent them off to London together. . . . What might not happen at Kew Gardens? . . . The minx will steal him from me. . . . Yes indeed, miss, love is an extraordinary thing! Oh God, that I had never heard the name of Harriet Smith! (*She crosses to fire.*)

SERLE *comes in.*

SERLE. Miss Bates to see you, ma'am.

EMMA. Oh — what is it, Serle?

SERLE. Miss Bates, ma'am.

EMMA. Miss Bates. Oh, ask her to step in, please, Serle.

MISS BATES (*behind* SERLE). Here I am, Miss Woodhouse.

EMMA (*rises*). Dear Miss Bates, how very kind of you to call. (*Kisses her on the cheek.*)

MISS BATES. Dear Miss Woodhouse, I merely came to thank you for all your kindness, such an evening as I shall never forget. The music, the friends, the food, everything perfection.

EMMA. Only the hostess lacked perfection. Dear

Miss Bates, can you forgive me? Truly I did not mean to be unkind. I meant it as a jest, but I had not thought to hurt you.

MISS BATES. Dear Miss Woodhouse, you need not apologise. So many other kindnesses have you shown me, surely I can forgive one little jest against me, and no one knows better than I do that I talk too much. Jane is for ever telling me about it, but somehow, I do not know how it is, I simply cannot help it.

EMMA (*she crosses to below sofa, tears in her eyes and voice*). But, Miss Bates, I was unkind. I am unkind and selfish and headstrong. I have no thought for others. I have been spoilt, and I am meddlesome to a degree. Mr. Knightley says it, so it must be true.

MISS BATES. You have heard of Jane's engagement to Mr. Churchill?

EMMA (*nods vigorously while she wipes her eyes.* MISS BATES *nods with her.*) No gentleman will ever want me with such a character as I have. So wicked as I am. (*She sits sofa.*)

MISS BATES (*she sits* L. *of* EMMA *on sofa*). Did you love him so very much?

EMMA (*thinking she means* MR. KNIGHTLEY, *nods.* MISS BATES *nods in sympathy.*) I think I have always loved him.

MISS BATES. And now he loves another.

EMMA. I am sure of it.

MISS BATES. Oh, please do not be in doubt, dear child; he does love her, and she loves him with all her heart.

EMMA *bursts into tears again, and* MISS BATES *tries to comfort her as*

The Curtain falls

SCENE II: *Early Afternoon in Summer*

The same. After lunch at the strawberry gathering party. Rays of brilliant summer sunshine flood the room as it pours in at the french windows.

SERLE *throws open the double doors and stands respectfully aside for the guests who are returning from the dining-room. The ladies wear their prettiest summer dresses and shady garden hats.*

MR. *and* MRS. ELTON, MISS BATES *and* MISS FAIRFAX *enter first, followed by* MR. WOODHOUSE *and* MR. WESTON.

MRS. ELTON *crosses to sit armchair* U.L. — ELTON *behind her.*

MRS. ELTON (*using her fan prodigiously, addressing all who will listen*). I declare the strawberry is everybody's favourite . . . delicious fruit. Though I infinitely prefer the cherry. Maple Grove had an abundance of cherries. Stooping to gather strawberries in the glaring sun tires one to death. I declare I am quite worn out. If we had not ceased for luncheon, I think I should have swooned.

MISS BATES (*sitting sofa with* JANE). And such a luncheon as our good friends have given us. The cold chicken a delight in itself, Mr. Woodhouse. An absolute delight, so tasty was the wing I had.

MRS. ELTON. An indoor luncheon at a strawberry party is a novel idea. Quite a rest from the sun, I suppose. So different from Maple Grove. Lunch on the terrace at Maple Grove. No terrace here — how could one have lunch on the terrace?

MR. WESTON (U.C. *with* MR. WOODHOUSE). Hartfield is my idea of the perfect residence. The size of the house, the rooms, the garden. Everything perfection. (*He crosses to above sofa.*)

MRS. ELTON (*at* JANE). What does the future Mrs. Churchill think? You must be all excitement to see your new home, Jane, dear. Enscombe is the finest estate in Yorkshire, I believe.

JANE. I understand Enscombe is quite large, but Mr. Churchill himself will be here soon, he will furnish you with all the details.

MRS. ELTON. Poor Mrs. Smallridge will be quite heartbroken when I tell her you have found a situation even more inviting than her own. I am all happiness for you in your great good fortune. (*Her tone implies that she is anything but all happiness.*)

JANE (*with some spirit*). My good fortune, Mrs. Elton, is in captivating Mr. Churchill's affection. Were his establishment no larger than the Vicarage I should not be less happy than I am now.

MRS. ELTON'S *fan suffers considerably while she thinks of a suitable reply.*

MRS. ELTON (*she rises*). A gentleman's affection and an establishment, no matter how small, must always be considered great good fortune and infinitely preferable to being a governess in even Mrs. Smallridge's family. Come, Mr. E., let us explore the meadows. The air indoors is stifling on such a day. (*Waves her fan briskly and snaps it together as she reaches the french windows.*)

MR. ELTON. Yes, Augusta, my love.

They go out at the french windows.

MR. WESTON. Poor Mr. Elton. Never have I seen such a change in any man. I swear he does not open his mouth at all but to say " Yes, Augusta, my love ", and I am convinced he is not allowed to have one opinion of his own, not even an unspoken one.

MR. WOODHOUSE (*he sits armchair* U.L.). I remember saying at the time how I thought he was very well off as he was. Marriage is a burden any man should avoid.

MR. WESTON (*he crosses to* R. *of armchair* U.L.). I cannot allow that, sir. I vow I am the happiest man in the world since my marriage to Mrs. Weston.

MR. WOODHOUSE. Poor Miss Taylor was very happy here at Hartfield with me and Emma.

MISS BATES. What excitement could there be without a romance going on? What other interest would there be for us but a scandal, a birth or a death? No, sir, I am all for marriage and glad with all my heart that dear Jane has made a match. Would that I had her opportunity.

JANE. Let us go into the garden, Aunt, and make the most of the sunshine.

MISS BATES. Then put up your parasol, Jane, dear. A bride with a blotchy skin would never do.

EMMA *and* MRS. WESTON *come in together, an older, wiser* EMMA.

EMMA. Serle is serving coffee in the summer-house.

MR. WOODHOUSE (*he rises, crosses* D.R.). Then let us go at once. Leave word with Serle to send Mr. Knightley to us if he should arrive, and Mr. Churchill too. Come, Miss Bates, give me your arm. Miss Fairfax?

MISS BATES (*coyly*). Thank you, sir.

JANE. Delighted, sir.

Takes MR. WOODHOUSE'S *other arm and they go out.*

MISS BATES. So comforting as a gentleman's arm always is.

They have gone.

MR. WESTON (*to* MRS. WESTON). Now, my love, I must make haste to Randalls for the feeding of the livestock. I shall return at once.

MRS. WESTON. Very well, my love. (*Sits armchair* U.L.)

EMMA. Pray do not be long, sir.

MR. WESTON (*gallantly*). No longer than I can help, ladies, you may be assured.

He goes out, leaving EMMA *and* MRS. WESTON.

EMMA (*distressed*). I confess that I cannot understand it. Never before has Mr. Knightley missed my strawberry party, and after he promised he would be here, too. You do not imagine something could have happened? An accident to the coach? Some illness contracted in London?

MRS. WESTON. My dearest Emma, if you but mention Mr. Knightley to me again I shall soon suspect you of being in love with him.

EMMA. Oh, madam, I am all but in despair. I have known I loved him since the day he went to London.

MRS. WESTON. Emma, my love!

EMMA. I am convinced he loves another; what is more, it is all my own doing. Never have I been so miserable. Not a word has he written since he went away, not one word, and now he has not come to my party.

MRS. WESTON. There is no doubt some good reason for the delay. Have you given Mr. Knightley any inkling that his overtures might be encouraged?

EMMA (*she rises, crosses to desk with a show of her old*

spirit). Decidedly not, as if I should. If a gentleman is sufficiently interested, let him find that out for himself.

MRS. WESTON (*rises, crosses to her*). My headstrong, foolish Emma. You would help everyone towards love except yourself.

EMMA. Yes, I am foolish and headstrong. I know it only too well, and through it I have lost the only man I could ever marry.

MRS. WESTON. But, Emma, dear, what of little Henry?

EMMA. Little Henry, what of him?

MRS. WESTON. You said if Mr. Knightley were to marry he would be done out of Donwell Abbey, his rightful inheritance.

EMMA (*the old* EMMA). Please, madam, do not put up more obstacles. Henry is but a child of six years old. He is too young to realise his loss.

SERLE *comes in.* EMMA *rises and goes to the fireplace, wiping her eyes.*

SERLE. Mr. Churchill. (*He stands aside for* MR. CHURCHILL *to come in.*)

MRS. WESTON. I was about to tell you Frank was expected this afternoon, and here he is before I have the chance. (FRANK *enters.*) If you will excuse me, I shall leave you and inform Jane of your arrival.

MRS. WESTON *goes out.*

FRANK (*to* EMMA). Tell me I am truly forgiven? (*Crosses to* EMMA.)

EMMA. There is nothing to forgive, sir; fortunately my affections were safe from all your false overtures.

FRANK. You cover me in shame.

EMMA. That is not at all necessary. You were in love — you had given your promise. I should have done the same in your position.

FRANK. This is what I have always felt about you, an appreciation of the same things.

EMMA. I believe there is a little likeness between us.

FRANK. More than a little; I hope we shall always be friends.

SERLE *comes in.*

SERLE. Mr. Knightley.

EMMA *starts so guiltily and is covered in such confusion that* FRANK *immediately guesses her secret.*

FRANK. So that is the way the wind blows. I wish you joy and I shall leave you to it.

He laughs gaily and runs out into the garden. EMMA *looks round wildly, takes fright and is about to follow him out when* MR. KNIGHTLEY *comes in. Their eyes meet. Both are confused.*

MR. KNIGHTLEY. Emma. (U.C.)

EMMA. Mr. Knightley. (D.R.)

MR. KNIGHTLEY. I should have been here before. The London coach was delayed.

EMMA. I thought you had forgotten, sir.

MR. KNIGHTLEY. Forget your party, Emma? You are not kind to suggest such a thing.

EMMA (*she sits sofa*). Forgive me, I am not quite myself . . . the sudden heat . . .

MR. KNIGHTLEY (*coming closer, sits beside her*). Do not grieve, dearest Emma. Time and your own excellent sense will heal the wound. I know you will not allow yourself to be broken by that damnable scoundrel's conduct. (*Takes her arm and pats her hand.*) He will soon be gone. I am sorry for Miss Fairfax, she deserves a better fate. But it is you who have suffered most.

EMMA. You are very kind, sir, but you are mistaken, and I must set you right. I am not, nor have I ever been, deeply in love with Mr. Churchill.

MR. KNIGHTLEY (*patting her hand*). My brave Emma, you do not need to put up a show for me. I understand.

EMMA. But I do assure you, sir, I am sincere. I may have been tempted by his attentions and perhaps allowed myself to appear pleased. To my shame, let me confess my vanity was flattered. He may have imposed on my feelings but he did not injure me.

MR. KNIGHTLEY. I have never had a high opinion of Mr. Churchill's character, but it is possible I may have underrated him. With such a woman as Jane Fairfax he has an excellent chance of happiness.

EMMA. I have no doubt of their being happy together. I believe them to be mutually and sincerely attached.

MR. KNIGHTLEY (*rises, crosses* L.C., *with a sigh*). He is a very fortunate young man indeed.

EMMA. You speak as if you envied him, sir.

MR. KNIGHTLEY. Yes indeed, I do envy him. I have some news for you, and I am very much afraid you will not smile when you hear it. It concerns a fair young friend of yours.

EMMA (*hardly daring to speak*). Harriet Smith?

MR. KNIGHTLEY. None other. You may guess the rest without my telling you. The news is of a wedding.

EMMA. You mean that you — she is going to be married?

MR. KNIGHTLEY. Married, and without delay. I cannot tell you how happy I am about it. I have for some time held a high opinion of the lady. She will be an excellent wife. Of course I cannot expect you to be pleased.

EMMA (*she rises, crosses* C.). Why should I not be pleased? What should it matter to me whether Miss Smith decides to get married or not?

MR. KNIGHTLEY. Did you not advise her against such a marriage?

EMMA (*in tears*). You have no right to torture me like this, sir. Is it not enough for you to see my heart is broken?

She tries to run away, he holds her close.

MR. KNIGHTLEY. My dearest Emma, I did not mean to upset you so. Why should it mean so much to you that Miss Smith should marry Mr. Martin? What can you have against him?

EMMA. Mr. Martin! What foolishness is this? Sir, you said just now that she was to marry . . .

MR. KNIGHTLEY. Mr. Robert Martin of Abbey Mill Farm.

EMMA. But I thought . . . Oh, I cannot believe it. You mean that he has proposed to her again? That she has accepted him?

MR. KNIGHTLEY. Yes, he came to London on some business for me. Isabella invited him to stay to dinner, and of course Harriet was there. They strolled in the garden. He made good his opportunity, proposed and was accepted.

EMMA. I cannot yet believe it.

MR. KNIGHTLEY. By the way, Robert called on her

legal guardian for consent to marry Harriet, and learned that her father is but a prosperous London tradesman. A pork butcher, I understand.

EMMA (*laughing*). A pork butcher! Oh, my poor Harriet!

MR. KNIGHTLEY. So you see your little friend is not belittling herself by any means.

EMMA (*she crosses to sit sofa*). What a fool I have been. So wrong in every circumstance. I have learnt many things since you went away, sir. How right you have always been about my character. How wrong I have been in everything; believe me, sir, I am truly humble now.

MR. KNIGHTLEY (*he crosses to behind sofa*). So humble that you could even have apologised to Miss Bates?

EMMA. Yes, sir, for I was deeply ashamed of my behaviour. You were indeed a friend to point out my fault.

MR. KNIGHTLEY. Friend it is, and I am afraid it always will be.

EMMA. What do you mean, sir?

MR. KNIGHTLEY. No matter. So now that Miss Smith and Mr. Martin are come together, it would seem all your wrongs have become rights.

EMMA (*passionately*). Believe me, sir, I shall never attempt to make another match while I live.

MR. KNIGHTLEY (*to sit* R. *of* EMMA *on sofa*). Only one more, dearest Emma, for dearest you will always be. Tell me, have I no chance of succeeding? Tell me at once.

EMMA. This to me. I am all astonishment, sir.

MR. KNIGHTLEY. I cannot make pretty speeches, Emma. If I loved you less, I might be able to talk about it more. But you know what I am.

EMMA. Yes, sir, I do.

MR. KNIGHTLEY. You have always borne the truth from me. Bear it now while I tell you how deeply, sincerely and tenderly I will love you for all my days.

EMMA. Oh, sir . . .

MR. KNIGHTLEY. And now all I ask is to hear your own beloved voice saying you will marry me.

EMMA (*moved as she has never been*). Oh, sir, I love you with all my heart and soul. (MR. KNIGHTLEY *takes her in his arms and holds her there.*) Never have I known such perfect happiness. (*Then, thunder-struck, she remembers.*) But, Mr. Knightley, I cannot marry you. Papa would never agree to my leaving him.

MR. KNIGHTLEY. I have thought it all out a thousand times. If he will but have me for a son-in-law, I shall quit Donwell and stay here at Hartfield while he lives.

EMMA. I appreciate the sacrifice, sir, but I do not think he will agree.

MR. KNIGHTLEY. Then I can but offer to wait until you are free.

EMMA. Oh, Mr. Knightley, sir . . .

MR. KNIGHTLEY. Emma, my love, do you not think you might now call me by my Christian name?

EMMA. Once, years ago, I did call you George to annoy you, and when you did not seem to mind I immediately decided against ever doing it again.

He takes her in his arms again. MISS BATES *comes in at this moment.*

MISS BATES (*she crosses to* C., *turns back, gasps*). Oh, Miss Woodhouse — shocking! Mr. Knightley, you of all people. I am surprised. In the drawing-room, too. I never guessed at such a thing.

MR. KNIGHTLEY. There is no need to be shocked, Miss Bates. Miss Woodhouse has done me the honour to say she will become my wife.

MISS BATES (*delighted*). A romance, how thrilling. Such a season of romances. Congratulations — congratulations, Miss Woodhouse. Dear Jane will be delighted when I tell her. (*She crosses to windows.*)

EMMA. Dear Miss Bates, for private reasons we would like the engagement kept secret.

MISS BATES. Another secret engagement! Quite a fashion. Jane will be pleased.

MR. KNIGHTLEY. Pray, Miss Bates, only you know our secret. Guard it for us, if you please.

MISS BATES. With my life, sir. . . . Not a word, Miss Woodhouse. (*She puts her finger to her lips, grins at them and hurries out.*) It shall be a secret, I promise.

EMMA (*she crosses* L.C.). Now there is no hope for us. Papa is bound to hear of it.

SERLE *comes in.*

SERLE. Miss Smith to see Miss Woodhouse.

EMMA (*to* MR. KNIGHTLEY). Has Harriet come back?

MR. KNIGHTLEY. She and Robert Martin travelled with me. I dropped them at Abbey Mill.

EMMA. Show Miss Smith in, Serle. (SERLE *bows and goes out.*) Dearest Harriet, only now do I realise how much I have missed her.

HARRIET *comes in all of a flutter.*

HARRIET (*going to* EMMA). Oh, Miss Woodhouse, dear Miss Woodhouse.

EMMA. My dear Harriet.

HARRIET. Has Mr. Knightley told you the news?

EMMA (*nods*). And I am delighted.

HARRIET. You are, Miss Woodhouse, you really are? I have not known how to face you.

EMMA. I was wrong before, Harriet. I ask your forgiveness.

HARRIET. When I found that Mr. Martin had loved me all this time, and how unhappy he was, I could not resist but to say yes, and really, Miss Woodhouse, Abbey Mill Farm is a very comfortable sort of house to live in.

MR. WOODHOUSE *comes in very distressed.*

MR. WOODHOUSE. Emma, my love, what is this I hear? It cannot be true.

EMMA. Dear Harriet, leave us alone with Papa for a moment. You will find many old friends in the garden anxious to see you.

HARRIET. Oh, thank you, Miss Woodhouse, thank you very much indeed.

She flutters out through the french windows into the garden.

MR. KNIGHTLEY (*pilots him to sofa*). Come and sit down, sir, and be comfortable.

MR. WOODHOUSE. Is it true that you have done this terrible thing to me, sir? Is it true you have stolen my Emma?

EMMA. Yes, Papa. Mr. Knightley has asked me to marry him.

MR. WOODHOUSE. And what have you said to the gentleman, Emma? Tell me you have refused.

EMMA. I have said I will marry him only if my dear Papa will give his consent.

EMMA *and* MR. KNIGHTLEY *lead* MR. WOODHOUSE *to sit sofa* D.R.

MR. WOODHOUSE. But, Emma, have you not always told me you would never marry? Such a comfort that has always been. Believe me, my love, you would do a great deal better to remain single. That is the advice I gave Mr. Elton; see how he has turned out.

EMMA. But, dearest Papa, I do not intend to desert you. You will not lose a daughter, but gain a son, and you know how fond you are of Mr. Knightley.

MR. WOODHOUSE. Only as a neighbour. (*Shakes his head at* MR. KNIGHTLEY.) I did not think you would play me false, sir.

MR. KNIGHTLEY. Believe me, sir, that has not been my intention. I do not think Emma has made it quite clear to you. If you would be so kind as to offer me your hospitality, I should take up my abode with you here at Hartfield.

EMMA. Think what an advantage to have Mr. Knightley always at hand, sir.

MR. WOODHOUSE. No, no, it will not do, I must think it over. No, no, it would not be the same.

EMMA. I love him, Papa, I love him.

MR. KNIGHTLEY. And I love Emma, sir, with all my heart.

MR. WOODHOUSE. The news has quite upset me, I am all of a tremble. It is not good for an old man to be upset.

MR. KNIGHTLEY. Perhaps a glass of Madeira wine, sir.

EMMA. Ring the bell for Serle.

MR. KNIGHTLEY *rings the bell.*

MR. WOODHOUSE. Just half a glass — in water, of course.

MRS. WESTON *comes in all excitement.*

MRS. WESTON. Dearest Emma, what is this I hear? Miss Bates has just said that you and Mr. Knightley . . . such a surprise. (*She kisses* EMMA.)

Both D.C.

EMMA. Miss Bates is too hasty by far. Papa has not yet given his consent, have you, Papa?

MR. WOODHOUSE. I will not have pistols held at my head, Emma.

SERLE *comes in.*

EMMA. Serle, please bring Mr. Woodhouse a glass of Madeira wine.

MR. WOODHOUSE. A whole glass, Serle, and no water.

SERLE. Yes, sir.

Goes out.

MR. WOODHOUSE (*to* MRS. WESTON). A fine upset on a summer's day, is it not, madam?

MRS. WESTON. Do not ask me to take sides, sir, you know how attached I am to you all. I could not bear a disagreement with any one of you.

JANE FAIRFAX *and* FRANK CHURCHILL *come in.*

JANE (*she crosses to* EMMA). Dear Miss Woodhouse, I am all happiness for you and Mr. Knightley. Congratulations, sir.

FRANK (D.R.). And mine too, sir. I wish you all the happiness in the world, dear Miss Woodhouse.

MR. WOODHOUSE. You are not right, sir, I will not have these congratulations forcing my hand.

EMMA. Where is Miss Bates, pray?

JANE. She went to find the Eltons.

FRANK. When last we saw her she was running towards the meadows.

HARRIET *comes in.*

HARRIET (*going to* EMMA). Oh, dear Miss Woodhouse, Miss Bates has just told me. I wish you joy. (*She embraces* EMMA. *To* MR. KNIGHTLEY) And you too, sir.

MR. WOODHOUSE. No more of this congratulating, if you please, I will not have it.

SERLE (*holding out wine on tray*). Your Madeira, sir.

MR. WOODHOUSE. Thank you, Serle; I am greatly in need of it. Pray bring me another. Never have I had such an upset.

EMMA. Serle, please bring some wine for our guests.

SERLE. Yes, ma'am.

He goes out.

EMMA. Pray, dear Papa, let us forget the whole incident. Neither Mr. Knightley nor myself would wish you to be upset.

MR. KNIGHTLEY (*he crosses to* L. *of* EMMA). I am at one with Emma, sir.

MR. *and* MRS. ELTON *come in from the garden followed by* MISS BATES. MR. *and* MRS. ELTON *cross* C., MISS BATES D.R.

MRS. ELTON. What is this I hear, Miss Woodhouse and Mr. Knightley? Who next, I wonder? See what an example we have set, Mr. E. Our marriage seems infectious.

MR. WOODHOUSE (*excited*). You are wrong, madam. Marriage is not only infectious, it is a positive plague. My daughter will not marry Mr. Knightley or anyone without my consent, whether he is to live here with us or no.

EMMA. I beg of you, dear Papa, do not upset yourself so. We should not have made it known.

MISS BATES. I told them all it was a secret, Miss Woodhouse, truly I did.

MRS. ELTON. If you ask my advice, you are very wise to put it off. A couple of my acquaintance near Maple Grove set up house with a mother-in-law, and all three separated by the end of the first quarter.

MR. ELTON. Yes indeed, Knightley, rather you than I. I would not live with an in-law for the world.

EMMA. You were not given the opportunity, sir.

FRANK. Elton, it would seem, thinks in-laws are out-laws.

Laughter from the ladies, especially MRS. ELTON, *who laughs louder than anyone.*

MRS. ELTON. You are a droll, sir.

MR. ELTON (*on his dignity*). Pray control yourself, Augusta.

SERLE *returns with a large silver tray and ten glasses of Madeira wine already poured out. He carries the tray round.* MR. KNIGHTLEY *and* FRANK CHURCHILL *help the ladies.*

HARRIET. I do not agree with Mr. and Mrs. Elton. When I marry Mr. Robert Martin next month we are to live with his family at Abbey Mill Farm, and I would not have it otherwise. I dote on good Mrs. Martin, who is the kindest lady in the world.

MISS BATES. Yet another romance, dear Miss Smith? I wish you great happiness. I am so pleased you have overcome all your disappointments so successfully. I would not be surprised if Mr. Woodhouse himself were to be the next. (*Giggles.*)

MR. WOODHOUSE. No, thank you, Miss Bates. I

cannot accept your kind suggestion.

MRS. ELTON. So you are to be married too, Miss Smith. Upon my word, husbands are two a penny nowadays.

HARRIET (*sweetly*). It is a pity you did not wait a little longer, Mrs. Elton, is it not?

EMMA *stifles her laughter as* FRANK CHURCHILL *tries to catch her eye.* MRS. ELTON'S *fan is dangerously active, but for once she is speechless.* MR. ELTON *pats her arm affectionately; this infuriates her and she raps him over the knuckles "playfully" and crosses* D.L. *to sit stool.* MR. WESTON *hurries into the room, greatly excited.*

MR. WESTON (*goes to his wife*). Oh, my love, such a terrible thing has happened.

MRS. WESTON (L.C. *by desk*). What is it, my love, what is it?

MR. WESTON. A calamity, Mrs. Weston, a calamity. The turkey house has been robbed entirely, not a turkey left.

MRS. WESTON. Oh, my love, how could such a thing have happened?

MR. WOODHOUSE. A robbery, sir, a robbery at Randalls?

MR. WESTON. I met good Mr. Cole on my way here; he has lost a score or so of sheep.

MR. WOODHOUSE. A robbery at Coles', our very neighbours! What next? Who could have been responsible for such a thing?

MR. WESTON. The gipsies, sir. The gipsies are in the neighbourhood again.

Gasps of excitement and astonishment from the ladies.

MR. WOODHOUSE (*greatly concerned*). Gipsies! Emma, my love, you are never to leave the house unattended. Soon the gipsies will get to know we are but an old man and a girl alone in the house. It will not be safe to retire to our beds at night. What are we to do? No one to turn to!

FRANK. Come, sir, it is not as bad as that.

MR. KNIGHTLEY. Churchill is right, sir.

MR. WOODHOUSE. Not so bad for virile young men like you and Churchill, sir. What is an old man like me to do? What could I do against a gipsy, sir?

EMMA. If you were to give your consent to our marriage, Papa, Mr. Knightley would always be here to protect us. Would you not, Mr. Knightley — George?

They both laugh.

MR. WOODHOUSE. So you would, sir. I had forgotten the gipsies. Why did you not remind me, Emma? How soon can you be married, sir? (*With rising excitement*) Do not delay, Emma, see to it at once. We must have the wedding without more ado.

MRS. WESTON (*to* MR. WESTON). Emma and Mr. Knightley are to be married, my love.

MR. WESTON. Emma and Knightley, that is a happy thought. Why did we not think of it before? Congratulations to you both.

MR. WOODHOUSE. Let us drink to the health of the future brides without delay.

MR. KNIGHTLEY (*raises his glass*). Miss Fairfax.

ALL. Miss Fairfax.

JANE *curtseys.*

MR. KNIGHTLEY. Miss Smith.

ALL. Miss Smith.

HARRIET *curtseys.*

MR. KNIGHTLEY. And my dear, dear Emma.

ALL. Miss Woodhouse.

EMMA *curtseys. All raise their glasses.*

Curtain

THE END

Printed in Great Britain by R. & R. CLARK, LIMITED, *Edinburgh.*